W9-CRW-811

Acknowledgements

The Chimo Project would like to thank the **Alberta Ministry of Children's Services** for providing the grant so that The Chimo Project could demonstrate the positive effect that Animal Assisted Therapy has on youth.

We would also like to thank all the therapists, staff and volunteers who dedicated their time to make this project possible.

This manual was created with the help and support of Cheryl Newton, Rose Marie Tremblay and Anne Nield.

The Chimo Project would also like to thank Emily Richard for appearing on the cover of this manual.

On the cover:

Certified Animal Assisted Therapy Shetland Sheepdog 'Pippin' (Rosecottage Mirage) Kristine Aanderson (BA) and Emily Richard

For more information about the implementation of Animal Assisted Therapy in professional settings, please go to our website:
www.chimoproject.com

Table of Contents

Introduction

This manual is designed for individuals working with or initiating a program for those suffering from fetal alcohol spectrum disorder or brain injury. It identifies the benefits of using animal assisted therapy with this population and suggests steps that can be taken to develop, operate, and evaluate such a program.

The bottom line is: it works! The unqualified love and affection of an appropriate animal combined with the skills of a caring therapist can help significantly improve the lives of those suffering from these often debilitating conditions.

The fact is that in other previous and current Chimo Project activities, this combination of therapist, animal and, often, volunteer has worked well for geriatric clients, clients in general private practice settings, and with adults and youth suffering from a variety of mental health issues. In other words, the process identified in these pages could be used for people suffering from many mental health ailments. This manual, however, is based on the experiences of the three-year demonstration project funded by the Alberta Department of Children's Services, dealing with Fetal Alcohol Spectrum Disorder (FASD) and brain-injured youth.

This manual should be read together with the first book produced by The Chimo Project, *"Improving Mental Health Through Animal Assisted Therapy"* co-authored by Liana Urichuck Ph.D. and myself. That book details how the animal may be used in specific ways to achieve therapeutic goals and also identifies other research done in this area.

By way of background, The Chimo Project was started by myself and named after the Blue Healer / Labrador cross that helped me survive my fifteen years as a member and a minister in the Alberta Legislature. Chimo was one of my beloved animal friends, others helped me through a difficult childhood and the ups and downs of life. I was therefore convinced at an early age that the love and affection of an animal can have a healing impact on humans and that, particularly in the area of mental health, society had not yet harnessed this most valuable resource in treating these illnesses.

The Chimo Project initially started 9 years ago. In year two it became a research project funded by Alberta Health and Wellness' Alberta Health Innovation Fund. The research project was designed to prove the benefit of using animals in the treatment of individuals suffering from mental illness, and also to identify various ways that animals could effectively be used in the treatment of mental illness. The project was 28 months in duration, and funding ended in October of 2002.

The research project was assisted by three organizations that were part of a General Chimo Advisory Committee. These three organizations were the Canadian Mental Health Association, The Edmonton Humane Society, and The Pet Therapy Society of Northern Alberta. The members involved were therapists and research advisors. This committee, with the advice of therapists on a Professional Chimo Advisory Committee, developed the framework for the original research project.

The Chimo Project recruited and hired an outside evaluator to carry out qualitative and quantitative data analysis on the research data collected. The research project also received approval from The Health Research Ethics Board at the University of Alberta. The Ethics Board limited the study to those with a primary diagnosis of anxiety or depression.

A worldwide literature search was conducted to identify the relevant background research in the use of Animal-Assisted Therapy (AAT) in mental health treatment and also to identify the gaps in the scientific proof of its benefits.

The key results from the Residential Care setting were:
- Youths overwhelmingly supported having the animal in therapy.
- Youths and therapists indicated that the animal's presence was therapeutic because youths felt the animal was of comfort to them, made them look

forward to coming to therapy, and accepted them for who they are.

- Therapy in general helps troubled youths perform better at home, school, and in the Residential Care facility; however, the youths receiving AAT showed greater benefits.

The key results from the Private Practice setting were:

- Clients were positive about the animal being in the therapy session.
- Therapists indicated that the animal assisted in establishing rapport with the clients, clients were more willing to come to therapy when the animal was present, the animal was of comfort to the clients during therapy, and the clients touched and talked directly to the animal.
- The results showed that AAT is as effective as traditional forms of therapy alone.

It was concluded that AAT does assist therapists in helping clients to overcome clinical depression and anxiety. The study also concluded that using animals in a targeted and goal-directed way significantly improves a therapist's ability to communicate with clients, and that clients embrace therapy more quickly.

It is our hope that the experiences identified in this manual and the material from the original research project, provide at least some of what is needed to bring this amazing animal benefit to those fighting to overcome the problems of fetal alcohol spectrum disorder and brain injury. **To the best of our knowledge, these projects, in Alberta, are the first projects of this kind in North America.** We hope that they provide many with a way to better health.

Dennis Anderson,
Director and Founder of The Chimo Project

Chapter 1: Animal Assisted Therapy, Fetal Alcohol Spectrum Disorder And Developmental Disabilities

What Is The Chimo Project?

What Is Animal Assisted Therapy (AAT)?

What Is Fetal Alcohol Spectrum Disorder (FASD)?

How Can AAT Help Clients With FASD?

Using AAT To Help Children With Developmental Disabilities

The AAT Pilot Program At Bosco Homes

What Is The Chimo Project?

The Chimo Project is an innovative, non-profit, charitable organization that assists in the development, planning, and implementation of animal assisted therapy in mental health programs at a wide variety of facilities.

As an organization we:
- advocate the use of animal assisted therapy in the community and petition mental health facilities to include AAT as part of their treatment offerings;
- provide site staff with professional orientation and The Chimo Project manuals;
- provide specialists that consult in information, direction, and animal screening;
- tailor-make each program;
- leaves all final program decisions to professionals;
- prepares the facility to operate programs on a continuing basis;
- recruit and orient appropriate animals and animal handlers;
- offer an animal assisted therapy 'in-a-box' program where we assist other organizations in the successful implementation of Animal Assisted Therapy programs in their own facilities.

We are constantly pioneering new ways to enable us to bring the benefits of animal assisted therapy to individuals suffering from mental health concerns.

What is Animal Assisted Therapy?

Animal Assisted Therapy (AAT) is a ***goal-directed*** intervention in which an animal is an integral part of the treatment process. A therapist who utilizes AAT operates from their professional foundation and facilitates change in a client through the client's interactions with an animal.

What distinguishes Animal Assisted Therapy from other types of therapy with animals?

Pet Therapy describes all types of therapeutic and mutually beneficial interactions between companion animals and people. Pet Therapy includes:
- Pet Visitation
- Animal Assisted Activities (AAA)
- Animal Assisted Therapy (AAT)

Pet Visitation is a scheduled program providing the opportunity for people/animal interaction in an informal, safe environment. <u>No specific outcomes are expected</u>, but it is regarded as therapeutic and very important to people living in facilities in our communities.

Animal Assisted Activities (AAA)
Although Animal Assisted Activities (AAA) may provide therapeutic results, there are <u>no written objectives</u> for individual clients. AAA involves the intentional use of companion animals to provide opportunities for motivational, educational, and recreational benefits. They are delivered by a professional, paraprofessional, or volunteer, and the animal **may** meet specific criteria. Examples include:
- educational programs (all ages, abilities);
- self-expression in literary/visual arts using animals as inspiration;
- craft projects (birdhouses, dog blankets);

Animal Assisted Therapy (AAT)

Animal Assisted Therapy (AAT) is <u>the most clinical interaction</u> and is defined by:

- goal-directed intervention;
- specific objectives for each session;
- animal meets specific criteria;
- the animal being an integral part of the structured treatment;
- direction/delivery by a health service provider working within the scope of his/her profession;
- a design to promote improvements in physical, social, emotional, or cognitive functioning;
- its ability to be used one-on-one or in group sessions;
- the requirement for documentation and evaluation.

What Is Fetal Alcohol Spectrum Disorder (FASD)?

Fetal Alcohol Spectrum Disorder (FASD) is also known as Fetal Alcohol Syndrome (FAS) or Fetal Alcohol Effects (FAE). They all refer to a series of mental and physical problems caused by fetal exposure to alcohol. FASD can vary in severity from no noticeable symptoms to severe mental and physical difficulties. This disorder is entirely preventable. A person cannot get FASD if not exposed to alcohol during pregnancy. There is no cure for FASD.

At this time, it is not known how many people suffer from FASD because it is difficult to accurately diagnose this disorder without knowledge of the prenatal alcohol exposure. FASD also has many symptoms that are similar to other mental disorders, which makes accurate diagnosis even more challenging.

Those diagnosed as suffering from FASD often have behavioral, intellectual, and physical difficulties. These problems will be lifelong, but in some cases the severity and type of symptom may change with age and life situation. Often, a person suffering from FASD can be helped to adapt to minimize the effect of the symptoms.

What Are The Symptoms Of Fetal Alcohol Spectrum Disorder Syndrome (FASD)?

FASD symptoms are complex and must be diagnosed by a team of professionals trained to differentiate FASD from other similar disorders.
Physical symptoms include:
- small head size
- smaller than average height and weight
- disproportionate facial characteristics
- low birth weight

- organ damage

Mental symptoms include:
- delayed achievement in the areas of visual, speech, and/or motor skills
- inattention
- intellectual delays
- hyperactivity
- sleeping problems
- lack of adaptive behaviors
- minimal social emotional ability
- sensory integration problems

Behavioral symptoms include:
- excessive vulnerability to peer influence
- short-sightedness, inability to forecast consequences of behavior
- mood swings
- inability to bond with others
- unpredictability
- inability/unwillingness to accept responsibility for actions
- self-centeredness
- constant need to get their own way
- resistance to change
- need for immediate gratification
- skill at shifting blame, reframing the truth (lying)
- inability to complete tasks
- genuine innocent and detached attitude
- lack of predatory intent
- arrested conscience development

How Can AAT Help Clients With FASD?

The participation of animals in therapy sessions can provide many valuable services when treating clients with fetal alcohol spectrum disorder.

The animals can be the incentive for the clients, encouraging them to come to therapy and to stay longer in the session. Animals can help to regulate mood by providing a sense of calm. When clients pet the animals, their stress may be reduced and their endorphin levels may rise. This may lead to the client becoming calmer and more able to work on difficult, sometimes frustrating issues that arise in therapy sessions.

Animals also provide a non-threatening invitation to participate in therapy. Animals often seek out those who are isolating themselves and bring them into the group. Therapy animals also provide an opportunity for the therapists and the client to communicate in a non-threatening, open manner by talking 'through' the therapy animal. It is sometimes difficult to approach life issues such as abuse or boundary violation with FASD clients. Interaction with the animal can provide an opportunity for the client to talk about these issues; for example, such as when a dog jumps up on a client or when a cat is kneading their laps. Difficult life issues can also be broached by using the animal as a replacement for the client. Instead of asking the client how they felt when they were removed from their families and placed in a foster home, a therapist can ask how the client thinks the animal felt when they were taken from their litter-mates and sent to live with a stranger.

Often when FASD clients are faced with the consequences of their behavior, they are resentful or do not understand why they are being punished. As a result, they often become defensive when a therapist questions them about their negative behavior. To avoid this, the therapist can use the therapy animal. Instead, of questioning the client directly about their behavior, therapists can say the animal 'heard' that the client was having trouble (got in a fight, ran away, got drunk) and that the animal is worried about the client. The therapist can then ask the client to tell the animal what happened. Because animals offer unconditional acceptance, the client does not have to become defensive when talking about their negative behavior to the animal.

Clients suffering from FASD often have difficulty understanding that behaviors have consequences, and have a great deal of trouble forecasting the consequences of their behaviors. Because it is difficult for FASD clients to apply abstract concept to concrete situations, a number of different approaches need to be taken when helping clients anticipate the outcomes of their behaviors. Many dogs are trained using positive training systems that teach the dog to anticipate the outcome of his actions. Positive training is based on the concept, "If I do what the trainer asks, I get a reward." If the animal does not perform the required task, then the animal does not receive the reward, or depending on the severity of the behavior, the animal may receive discipline, such as "No!" Good animal training systems also teach the trainers to anticipate the reaction of the animal and plan for the animal's success. A trainer learns: "If I lift this treat over the dog's nose, the dog will probably sit down." Teaching the client an animal training system offers them an opportunity to learn about behaviors and consequences in a positive light. Training the therapy animal also provides many other valuable learning experiences for clients with FASD, such as frustration control, empathy, confidence building, and how to set up a situation for success.

Animals can also provide comfort. Clients with FASD often have difficult, trauma-filled lives. Often the clients need to be comforted, but because of professional ethics, a therapist is not allowed to hug or touch a client to provide the much needed comfort. A therapy animal will never be accused of intentional unethical contact with a client, so the animal is free to comfort the client when it is needed most.

These are just some of the ways that a therapy animal can help a client suffering the effects of Fetal Alcohol Spectrum Disorder (FASD). There are other goals that the animal and therapist can help the child work toward, such as:

- anger Management
- relaxation
- rapport or relationship building
- increasing social interactions
- increasing participation in activities
- improving peer relations
- improving eye contact
- improving voice tone
- bonding
- appropriate touch
- trust
- dealing with feelings
- developing patience and understanding
- building self esteem and self confidence
- promoting empathy

Utilizing animals to help clients with Fetal Alcohol Spectrum Disorder (FASD) provides valuable opportunities to work through symptom-specific behaviors. Animal assisted therapy is an innovative way to reach clients who often have trouble succeeding in traditional therapy.

Using AAT To Help Children With Developmental Disabilities

Animal Assisted Therapy offers a significant opportunity to help children with developmental disabilities reach their therapeutic goals. The Chimo Project works with a variety of organizations across Canada and around to world to institute Animal Assisted Therapy programs. We help create facility policies, train therapists, recruit and certify therapy animals and develop evaluation processes. The Chimo Project has trained therapists from a wide range of fields who work with organizations such as Central Okanogan Child Development Association (COCDA) to use AAT to help clients and their families living with developmental disabilities.

A number of studies have shown the promise of using AAT to help children with developmental disabilities:

Martin and Farnum (2002) investigated the effect of AAT on children with pervasive developmental disorders. The children (aged 3-13) were exposed to three conditions; non social toy (ball), stuffed dog toy and live dog. When the children were interacting with the live dog they exhibited a **more playful mood**, were **more focused** and were **more aware of their social environments.**

A study by Oakley and Bardin (1998) shows the effect of AAT on children recovering from traumatic brain injury. In treatment sessions at St Mary's hospital for children in New York, the Occupational Therapists incorporated a dog into therapy sessions in order to satisfy specified goals. The child then become more **motivated** and **excited to participate** in the task, and eventually **attained the goals quicker** than anticipated and theses changes were present **even after the dog has left.**

Lieber (2003) conducted a ten-week study where the AAT dogs worked with children in their special education elementary school. *Parents, school counselors and special education teachers noted that the* children were **less disruptive,** formed **better peer relationships, showed improved communication skills** with adults, better ability to **cope with anxiety** and **better overall behavior.**

Tests show that stroking dogs **decreases the blood pressure** of children and adults**, even when performing an unpleasant task simultaneously** (Davies, 1998). This last study demonstrates how a therapist can use AAT during the therapy session involving an unpleasant task (such as stretching or completing a puzzle/test) to reduce stress/anxiety, even when the animal is not at the center of the task.

Animal Assisted Therapy is not a modality in and of itself. It is the use of strategies to achieve goals that can help maximize client strengths by enhancing traditional therapies. In our work at The Chimo Project, we have found dozens of goals that can be aided through the use of AAT. The most common goals that we see used in AAT with positive results include:

- Decrease in anxiety
- Increase in participation/attendance
- Increase in motivation to participate in the session
- Increase social interactions
- Decrease in depression

References :

Davis, J.H. (1998) Animal-facilitated therapy in stress mediation. Holistic Nursing Practice 2:75-83
Lieber, J. (2003). Animal Assisted Therapy for elementary students with emotional and behavioral disorders.

Dissertation Abstracts International Section B: The Sciences and Engineering. 63(7-A).

Oakley, D. and Bardin, G. (1998) The potential benefits of animal assisted therapy for children with special needs. (www.kidneeds.com)

Martin, F. and Farnum, J. (2002). Animal-Assisted Therapy for Children with Pervasive Developmental Disorders. *Western Journal of Nursing Research. 24(6)*, pp 657-670.

The AAT Pilot Program At Bosco Homes

The Chimo Project helps clients suffering from Fetal Alcohol Spectrum Disorder (FASD) at two residential youth facilities in the Edmonton, Alberta area. The pilot program for using animal assisted therapy to treat clients suffering from fetal alcohol spectrum disorder was developed at Bosco Homes, and the lessons learned from this pilot program helped as The Chimo Project established the second treatment facility program at the Yellowhead Youth Center. Currently, The Chimo Project's animal assisted therapy programs are operating at three treatment sites of Bosco Homes and at the Yellowhead Youth Center.

Bosco Homes
The Chimo Project provided consulting and assistance for program development at Bosco Homes. This development included:
- Policies and Procedures,
- Program Goals,
- Strategies and AAT Uses,
- Volunteer Handler Orientations,
- Therapist and Client Questionnaires as Outcome Measures.

This development was completed with the program managers and therapists from Bosco Homes for a custom fit to their clientele and therapy programs.

Other areas covered included:
- Liability,
- Risk Management,
- Allergen and Zoonoses Control Techniques

A new policies and procedures document specific AAT was developed for implementation. Current site pet visitation policies were left in place as their directives and usages are completely different from those of the clinically-based, goal-directed AAT sessions.

Several program managers, psychologists, recreational therapists, occupational therapists, house managers, and a special education teacher have been fully trained to use AAT strategies and techniques as an adjunct to their regular therapy and in working towards achieving program goals for their clients. They work out of all Bosco Homes sites mentioned above.

Appropriate, screened volunteer handlers were recruited and trained, and their animals were screened for health, obedience, and aptitude for the intimate nature and special needs of working in an AAT session. Additional developments included building a permanent on-site dog run with a dog house to care for the needs of visiting AAT animals. On-site work was accomplished via maintenance workers and as skill-learning tasks for the youths. The dog run and dog house were donated by friends of Bosco Homes.

Policies / Procedure / Outcome Measures Developed
The following policies, procedures, outcome measures, and forms are the result of the development meetings between the consultants of The Chimo Project, and program managers, mental health therapists, and legal advisors of Bosco Homes. They address the current standards of practice about infection, allergen, and zoonoses (the transmission of diseases between animals and humans) control and risk management. Examples of the developments at this site are listed in the following table:

Bosco Homes: Policies / Procedures Developed
Waiver Release Form
Global Policies for AAT Programs
Outcome Measures: Therapist Questionnaire
Outcome Measures: AAT Session Tracking Sheet
Outcome Measures: Client Questionnaire
Fetal Alcohol Spectrum Disorder (FASD) (information sheet
AAT Group and Individual Supervisions (information sheet for
On-Site Supervision (information sheet for volunteer animal
AAT Incident Report Form
AAT Intervention Planning Worksheet

Preliminary Program Evaluation

Therapy started in September of 2004, and initial results were significant. Bosco Homes has been using AAT effectively and has been reporting outstanding, positive results from the use of AAT with the youths with FASD. The animals are connecting with and reading the needs of the youths. The youths are better able to verbalize and communicate their feelings when the animal is present.

Chapter 2: First Steps

Site Assessment

Getting Everyone On Board – Maintenance, Outside Professions

Dealing With Obstacles

Drafting Policy And Procedures For The Facility

Insurance

Recruiting Interested Therapists

Determining The Number Of Possible Clients Suited For AAT

Training The Therapists

Deciding Staff Animals Or Volunteer Animals?

Determining If Therapists/Staff Are Interested In Training Their Own Pets

Drafting A Work Plan

Example Work Plan

Preparing An Evaluation Plan

Example Evaluation Plan

Site Assessment

It is important to evaluate the potential site before beginning an animal assisted therapy program. This evaluation will spot any problem areas early on – before they become issues that could jeopardize the program. It also gives an opportunity to examine the strengths that a facility has and how to incorporate an AAT program in a way that capitalizes on those assets.

The Facility
Will there be support for creating an animal assisted therapy program at the facility? Is there funding available for any costs? Are there administrators that can assist with the program? What is the general attitude towards having animals at the facility? Is the facility in good standing with regulatory bodies?

Site Characteristics
Where can the therapy take place? How much space is available for the therapy area? What is the floor covering in those areas? Is there a way to separate therapy areas from those with allergies or fear of the animals? Is the temperature appropriate for the type of therapy animal? Where can the animals exercise and eliminate? What types of animal activities would be appropriate for the facility? Could animals have long walks around the facility or run in an enclosed off-leash area?

Administration and Policy
What is the attitude of the administration towards an animal assisted therapy program? Would they be willing to help the program when needed? Is there a volunteer coordinator for volunteer handlers? What is the facility's policy about having animals on the property? Was the policy originally made for animal friends or for therapy animals? What is the policy for certifying animals or allowing animals onto the property?

What is the policy concerning animal misbehavior? If there is new policy required, would this be setting a precedent? Are there animal policies for similar programs in the area? Is there insurance for animal assisted therapy?

Service Characteristics

What kinds of treatments are available for the clients at the facility? Is there one-on-one therapy? Is there group therapy? Are the sessions optional or mandatory? What are the global goals for treatment at the facility? How would AAT be incorporated into these characteristics?

Infrastructure

Who is responsible if an animal has an accident? Will extra time be incurred by housekeeping staff for clean-up? What happens if the animal destroys something on the property? How many animals will be on site? What kinds of animals will be on the property? How long will those animals be there? How will allergies be dealt with?

Staff

Who is interested in operating an animal assisted therapy program at the facility? What kinds of therapists are employed at the facility? Is there someone interested in being the AAT site manager? For those who are not interested in being involved in the AAT program, what are their attitudes towards animals in the facility? What are the main concerns of the therapists regarding the application of AAT?

Residents/Clients

What are the client demographics? Age, presenting diagnosis, cultural background, mental and physical level of functioning, history, and current life situation are all important. How many clients are suitable for AAT? How many clients are *not* suitable for animal assisted therapy? What is the consent process for being part of an AAT program? How would AAT fit in with normal treatments the client received?

Safety Concerns

What are the temperatures in and around the facility? Are there places that are too hot or too cold for animals? What is the policy regarding medication at the facility? Are clients in charge of their own medications meaning that the animals might come into contact with them? <u>Or Could animals come in contact with the clients medication?</u> How will the animals relax/de-stress between therapy sessions? Do the clients have animal abuse in their backgrounds?

How does the facility deal with pests? If they use poison, then that policy must be changed before animals can be introduced to the facility.

None of the answers to these questions represents a 'do-or-die' problem for animal assisted therapy at the facility. They simply highlight strengths and weaknesses of the facility that need to be addressed before animal assisted therapy can be implemented.

Getting Everyone On Board

The first step in introducing animal assisted therapy (AAT) to a facility is making sure that all people involved feel comfortable with the program's concept and potential. In order to begin an AAT program, a meeting should be planned with all the individuals who will be directly and indirectly involved with the program. This meeting should cover the details of the program and its implementation including: What is AAT? How will it be applied at this facility? Who will be involved? What animals will be used? What certification process will these animals go through? Where in the facility will AAT likely be taking place? And how will concerns be addressed?

It is not likely that everyone at a facility will initially think that animal assisted therapy is a great idea. Possibly there will be a staff member, a therapist, a maintenance worker, a client or a client's family member who thinks that AAT at the facility is a bad idea. Sometimes these people have specific concerns that can be addressed by taking the time to provide them with information. A social worker who doesn't believe that AAT can help one of their charges can be presented with the research data indicating AAT to be an effective treatment modality. Staff worried that the AAT program will be a lot of work and ultimately won't do any good, can be shown examples of facilities where AAT programs have been running with great success. Often the main concern is someone being required to take time out of their schedule to help with the AAT program. If this is a concern for someone not directly involved in the AAT program, the person should be assured that they will not have to take time to deal with the AAT program. If the concern has been raised by someone who is involved directly with the AAT program, processes should be streamlined so that their tasks can be completed it in the shortest time possible.

The important thing to remember is that even those people who are not comfortable with the idea of animal assisted therapy may play an important role at the facility and have valid concerns. They should not be viewed as 'hard-liners' who need to be steamrollered in order to get a program underway. It is best to find out what their concerns are and develop a compromise so that everyone is happy, or at least appeased. Helpful procedures may include placing a towel/sheet on the client's lap when they are interacting with the animal so that family members do not have to do extra laundry due to animal hair, or having animals only in designated areas outside so that maintenance workers don't have to worry about a dog digging up their landscaping or that they may have to pick up dog poop.

Addressing the concerns of hesitant individuals concerns may result in changes that are better for the program in the long run and represent an improvement to AAT at the facility.

Dealing With Obstacles

Regardless of where an animal assisted therapy program is being established, four main concerns will almost always be raised: space, time commitment, liability, and allergies.

Space
Some people believe that a facility needs rolling hills and green fields to establish an animal assisted therapy program. While it is true that having many acres of space does provide a solution to some problems, it is by no means a necessity.

Many animal assisted therapy programs operate successfully in downtown office tower environments. The minimum space requirements include: one room large enough to accommodate the therapist, the client, and the therapy animal and a space for the animals to exercise. The exercise requirement can be fulfilled by as little as a walk down the street. If room space is a major consideration, then the program may want to investigate the use of smaller therapy animals. The space requirements of an English Mastiff dog are far greater than those for a Pomeranian. If exercise requirements are a concern, the choice of a different therapy animal may be the solution. Many small dogs require minimal exercise (running around the office will often suffice). If a place to curb the animal is a concern, then training a smaller dog to eliminate indoors in a designated area is a possibility. An excellent solution to all of these problems (office space, exercise and elimination) would be to use a trained therapy cat.

Time Commitment
Many therapists and staff members are concerned that animals that are not theirs will become their responsibility. This is a valid concern and one that needs to be addressed. In an animal assisted therapy program, there is only one person who is responsible for the animal – the handler. Other staff members may volunteer to help with the care of the animal (depending

on the policy of the facility), but this commitment should never be a requirement.

Many therapists are concerned with the amount of time it will take to learn a new treatment program and how much extra time it will take to perform AAT. Because AAT is an adjunct therapy, there is no need for the therapist to change their counseling style. The animals simply help the therapy run better. After a short series of training sessions, the therapists will be able to practice AAT and see the benefits it produces. There is more information on how to persuade hesitant therapists in the *Recruiting Therapists* section of this manual.

One advantage to remember about animal assisted therapy is that it is not only the clients who benefit from the animals; the therapists and staff members benefit as well! The results of a number of programs in a variety of different locations can attest to the positive effect on staff members and therapists. At a mental health hospital the staff reported that the therapy animal helped bring the staff together and produced a team-building effect. In one prison, the guards remarked that the therapy animals helped to ease the relations between prisoners and the guards. The presence of an animal increases positive communication between the handlers, clients, staff members, and therapists. Everyone benefits from an AAT program, not just the clients.

Liability
Many facilities want to know who is responsible for the behavior of the animal. There is only one answer to that question: the handler. No one else is responsible for the animal. The handler is responsible for the animal's well-being as well as for the animal's behavior on site.

The most important factor when considering liability is that negative incidents are not likely to occur with screened therapy animals and trained AAT therapists and animal handlers. Having clear policies and procedures is another method of limiting liability. If a facility and handler do everything in their power to ensure the safety and well-being of the clients when they are around the animal, it is easier to deal with a problem should one arise. In the seven years that The Chimo Project has been running, there has never been a single negative incident. This is due to the intense screening that therapy animals and handlers receive prior to entering a therapy facility as well as the extensive policies and procedures developed at all the facilities involved.

Most insurance companies neither include nor exclude animal assisted therapy, so it is necessary to check with each insurance provider. After an incident has occurred this is *not* the time to check insurance. Some options for insurance for animal assisted therapy programs are:

> Facility insurance – almost every mental health facility needs insurance to operate; it may be possible to have an AAT rider attached to the policy
>
> Pet therapy groups – many pet therapy organizations have insurance for their members who visit community facilities
>
> Homeowners' insurance – this often covers animal friends of the homeowner and any damage they may do off the owners property.

Allergies
It is possible that staff of clients at the facility will be allergic to certain animals. There are a series of questions to ask when the issue of allergies is brought up. Is this a perceived allergy or a real allergy? Some clients (or their families) and staff may not want to participate in AAT or have it at their facility, so the excuse of allergies is used. If you believe that this may be the case, then it is important to find out what the root cause of the resistance to an animal assisted therapy program is and to address it. In one prison system, an inmate claimed that she was so allergic to dogs she could not clean the floors (one of her chores at the prison) in the room where the animal therapy occurred. However, after seeing the benefits of being involved

in the AAT program, she joined the program and has since become one of their most successful dog trainers.

If the allergies are legitimate, then have the individuals tested for allergies? Some people have a single reaction and then avoid animals without being tested for allergies. The perceived animal allergy may be a reaction to a certain food or hay fever rather than caused by the animal. It is also possible that the animal came into contact with the real allergen (e.g., rolled in a field of pollen), and the person received a secondary reaction.

Has the person ever been on allergy medication? Would they be willing to consider it? Sometimes a simple solution for allergies is for the person in question to receive allergy shots.

What specific animals are they allergic to? Not all allergies are to 'furred animals'. Some allergies are species specific. How severe are their reactions to animals? Luckily, most animal allergies are not as severe as food allergies. The grooming a handler must do to a therapy animal may be enough to remove the dander and hair that cause reactions. It may be possible for animals to avoid direct contact with the person. They may be able to attend group sessions (or even individual therapy) with the instructions that they cannot pet the animal, but still participate. It may be necessary for the animal therapy room to be cleaned before the allergic individual can be brought into it. With more severe cases, it may be necessary to establish routes that the animals will take into and out of the facility to ensure that the animal and the allergic individual do not cross paths. As soon as it is identified that the facility has an individual who is allergic, regardless of any other interventions, a strict hand washing procedure should be implemented.

When Dr. Thomas was first implementing the Eden Alternative[1] he was horrified when he discovered that a nurse had gone into anaphylactic (allergenic) shock and had to be rushed to the hospital. He thought that the program including the resident animals would be shut down. However, it turned out that the nurse had been allergic to latex.

The most interesting part of this story was not what the nurse was allergic to, but how it was dealt with by the facility. The facility took all necessary precautions to ensure this nurse's safety. They gave her non-latex gloves to wear and made her aware of the locations in the facility where latex was present. Dr. Thomas reflected that if the allergy had been due to the animals at the facility, there would have been no hesitation to remove them entirely[2].

Dr. Thomas recommends that programs who find themselves dealing with staff or clients with animal allergies take the approach of the nurse with the latex allergy. Keep the person away from the allergen, and notify them of the specific locations in the facility where their allergen may be present. This presents a win-win situation. The animal assisted therapy program can continue, and the individual is able to continue working without being unduly affected by their allergies.

---

[1] A program for long-term care facilities that incorporates animals, plants and children.
[2] *Life Worth Living: How Someone You Love Can Still Enjoy Life in a Nursing Home - The Eden Alternative in Action* by William H. Thomas (1996)

Drafting Policy And Procedures For The Facility

When implementing an animal assisted therapy program at a facility, policies and procedures must be set in place for the program. Some facilities will require very strict policies and procedures that outline every detail of the animal assisted therapy program. Other facilities require policies and procedures that document the general direction of the program. These documents help protect everyone involved with the AAT program, as well as ensuring good communication between different departments.

A global policies and procedures document includes policies on how the therapy animals are to be used, the training required for a therapist to use an animal in a session, the certification requirements for a therapy animal, the humane treatment of the therapy animals, a client policy that reflects the minimum performance requirements for continued participation in the AAT program, and the hand washing policy. If volunteers are used, the document should include policies regarding volunteer animal handler minimum performance requirements for continued participation in the AAT program. Also clearly outlined should be the emergency procedures and reporting guidelines.

Procedures that should be developed for an animal assisted therapy program at a facility include risk management and safety procedures such as program logistics; animal and client screening procedures; volunteer animal handler screening criteria; sanitation and infection control procedures (e.g., hand washing, disposal of animal waste); designated locations for animal toileting, feeding, watering, exercising, and housing; emergency or unplanned incident procedures (e.g., incident reports, procedures for identification and discontinuation of unwanted interactions or behaviors between clients and animals); and procedures for periodic safety checks of animal housing and equipment. Also developed should be Quality Assurance Procedures, including volunteer animal handler and staff training procedures (initial and on-going); AAT staff procedures and involvement, client participation procedures; and utilization review procedures including measures of efficiency, effectiveness, and efficacy.

The policies and procedures document should include the contingency plan for dealing with an animal causing harm to or being harmed by a client. Incident reports should be clearly explained and provided to all individuals who will be involved in the animal assisted therapy program.

A sample Global Policies and Procedures document and Incident Report form is available in the index of this manual.

Insurance

Acquiring insurance for an animal assisted therapy program is a basic requirement for the safety of everyone involved in the program. All major facilities have global insurance policies, and often the AAT program can be added to the insurance policy. When a facility (or sister facilities funded by the same organization) already has insurance in place for community animal visitation programs or for client's animal friends visiting them at the facility, then the additional coverage for animal assisted therapy is simple to acquire.

If a facility is unable to gain coverage for an animal assisted therapy program, then there are other options.

Non-Profit animal visitation organizations provide insurance for dogs they have personally screened for health and temperament during the course of volunteer visits to approved facilities.

Homeowners' and Renters' Insurance covers bodily injuries to others, but if a dog bites a client and the client sues for damages, it will have to be shown that rigorous controls were in place to prevent the incident.

Professional Liability Insurance policies will vary, but many neither include nor exclude coverage for bodily injury as a direct or indirect result of using animal-assisted therapy.

Regardless of which solution is adapted for the animal assisted therapy program, optimal protection is provided by requiring all participants in the program to sign a waiver releasing all parties from liability.

How different professionals can use AAT

Psychologists

These professionals are concerned with the psychological functioning of a client. They help clients address and moderate psychological and behavioral symptoms of FASD. Their focus is to increase adaptive psychological functioning. One of the main benefits of using AAT is that it helps the client bond to the therapist. Without this trusting bond, the therapy process is almost impossible.

Psychologists can use AAT to help clients with FASD achieve treatment goals such as:

- Increase ability to bond
- Develop rapport
- Foster relationships
- Address emotions
- Promote empathy
- Build self-esteem
- Provide a sense of control
- Decrease stress
- Dealing with grief and loss
- Providing emotional safety
- Reduce abusive thoughts and behaviors
- Address issues surrounding anxiety, depression and ADHD

Psychiatrists

These professionals specialize in the prevention, diagnosis and treatment of mental illnesses. They order tests, prescribe and monitor medications and practice psychotherapy. Psychiatrists can use AAT in the same way that Psychologists use AAT in the achievement of a client's treatment goals.

Animal assisted therapy has also been indicated as beneficial for helping provide effective diagnostic clues when assessing patients (Brickle, 1980).

Mental Health Nurses

Mental Health Nurses work closely with other professionals to enable, educate and encourage clients through their therapeutic process. They help therapists monitor treatment plans, encourage clients to work on their treatment goals away from therapy sessions and monitor medications; including their effectiveness and their side effects.

Mental Health Nurses can use AAT to help clients achieve their treatment goals by:

- Providing encouragement and routine for adhering to medication timetable
- Decreasing stress
- Transferring AAT work in therapy sessions to a practical setting

Occupational Therapists and Recreational Therapists

Occupational Therapists are concerned with helping clients participate in the activities of daily living. They help clients with social-emotional, physical, cognitive, communication and adaptive behavior challenges. The focus is on learning new skills and overall functioning performance.

Recreational Therapists seek to promote health and wellness of the client in the areas of leisure, lifestyle and community reintegration. The focus is on learning new skills and overall functioning related to recreation and community.

Due to the physiological setbacks present in many sufferers of FASD, occupational and recreational therapy can provide key improvements in functioning.

These therapists can use AAT in four main areas, cognitive function, physical function and psychosocial function.

Cognitive goals that use AAT for clients with FASD include:

- Increasing attention span
- Encouraging adaptive behaviors
- Increase problem solving
- Improve sensory integration
- Encouraging communication/verbalization

- Improving memory

Physical goals that use AAT for clients with FASD include:
- Improve motor skills
- Improve refined skill acquisition
- Increase motivation for treatment
- Improve daily living skills

Psychosocial goals that use AAT for clients with FASD include:
- Improve interpersonal skills
- Increase self-expression
- Addressing emotions of self and others
- Increase socialization
- Stress management

Child and Youth Care Workers
These professionals often work in residential facilities. They often attend to the clients for 'the other 23 hours a day' – when they are not in therapy with another practitioner. They help encourage and reinforce the daily routine at the facility, support clients in achieving their treatment goals outside therapy sessions and provide counseling when a situation arises.
These professionals can use AAT to:
- Provide encouragement/reward/enforcement for daily routine
- Encourage proper behavior management
- Provide additional interest to activities program
- Encourage attendance at optional therapy groups
- Transfer AAT work in therapy sessions to a practical setting
- Increase communication
- Increase self-esteem
- Decrease stress
- Enhance group cohesion in the residential facility

Teachers and Teacher's Aides

Teachers and Teacher's aides encourage learning and optimum functioning in a learning environment. These professionals can use AAT in the classroom to:

- Decrease stress
- Encourage focus
- Improve information retention
- Reduce worries/thoughts of failure
- Provide incentive for correct behaviors
- Encourage persistence in the face of setbacks
- Improve self-esteem
- Spark an interest in learning

For more information about activities and interventions that can be used by a variety of practitioners, please read:
Gommonley, Howie, Kirwin, Zapf, Frye, Freeman and Stuart-Russell (1997); *Animal Assisted Therapy - Therapeutic Interventions;* The Delta Society.WA: Renton

Recruiting Interested Therapists

The single greatest challenge with recruiting therapists into an animal assisted therapy program is the time involved. Any change in a therapists' current practice indicates more work for the therapist, who is usually already very busy. The time incurred in receiving training in AAT and the extra time in each session (new session plans, organizing the animal's presence and completing evaluations) represent time that most therapists simply do not have.

However, the time incurred in training and practicing animal assisted therapy is far outweighed by the benefits to the therapeutic process. Often once therapists have received their training and start seeing results in their therapy sessions, they become excited about the program and the extra time required is no longer a major consideration.

The second greatest challenge is the 'progressive' nature of AAT. Animal assisted therapy is not a common method of treatment, and therapists will have questions about the efficacy of this new type of treatment.

Animal assisted therapy has been indicated as being successful in aiding with dozens of problems. The original Chimo research Project found that AAT was effective in treating Depression and Anxiety. Other studies on AAT have found that it is a valid treatment for many disorders including Anxiety[3], Schizophrenia[4], Emotional and Behavioral Disorders[5] Personality disorders[6], and Dementia Alzheimer's Type[7].

Animal assisted therapy has also been shown to help psychological concerns such as self-esteem[8], social

---

[3] (Barker & Dawson, 1998)
[4] (Barak, Savorai, Mavashev & Beni, 2001)
[5] (Lieber, 2003)
[6] (Sato, Senjo, Tanaka & Miyazaki, 2003)
[7] (Beyersdorf & Birkenhauer, 1990),
[8] (Bergesen, 1989)

interactions[9] children experiencing parental divorce[10], lack of communication[11], and increasing attendance in therapy sessions[12] – just to name a few. For more details, the Delta Society (www.deltasociety.org) has an extensive listing of research articles focused on the benefits of animal assisted therapy.

When speaking with all therapists, it is important to indicate the benefits and the challenges involved with an AAT program. Address their concerns and focus on the positive aspects of AAT. Often it is valuable to give a ½ hour introduction to animal assisted therapy, so that the therapists can learn more about AAT without having to expend major time and effort. Informal meetings can also provide information and let the therapists feel comfortable before continuing with animal assisted therapy.

Who can carry out animal assisted therapy?

Any professional who is accredited via an external organization can receive training to use animal assisted therapy in their sessions.
Common examples of individuals involves in the treatment team include:
 Psychologists
 Psychiatrists
 School Counsellors
 Mental Health Nurses
 Physical Therapists
 Occupational Therapists
 Recreational Therapists
 Child and Youth Care Workers
 Speech Language Pathologists

---

[9] (Hunt, Hart & Gomulkiewicz, 1992),
[10] (Hoff & Bergler, 2001
[11] Curtright and Turner. (2002).
[12] Kelly, 2002.

Teachers
Teaching Aides

Different professionals will use animal assisted therapy in different ways. The following listing is by no means mutually exclusive. It is meant to provide an outline for understanding the different treatment modalities that can be enhanced by using AAT.

For information on how these different types of professionals can use AAT within their treatment modalities, please see the appendix of this manual.

References:

Brickle. (1980). A review of the roles of pet animals in psychotherapy with the elderly. *International Journal of Aging and Human Development* 12:2

Barak, Savorai, Mavashev & Beni. (2001). Animal-Assisted Therapy for elderly schitzophrenic patients: A one-year controlled trial. *American Journal of Psychiatry.* Vol 9(4). American Psychiatric Assn.

Barker and Dawson. (1998). The Effects of Animal Assisted Therapy on Anxiety Ratings of Hospitalized Psychiatric Patients. *Psychiatric Services.* 49(6).

Bergesen. (1989). The Effects of Pet Facilitated Therapy on the Self-Esteem and Socialization of Primary School Children. *Paper presented at the 5ᵗʰ Annual Conference on Human-Animal Interactions.* Monaco.

Beyersdorf & Birkenhauer. (1990). The Theraputic use of Pets on an Alzheimer's Unit. *American Journal of Alzheimers's Care and Related Disorders and Research.* 5.

Curtright and Turner. (2002). The Influence of a stuffed and live animal on communication in a female with Alzheimers Dementia. *Journal of Medical Speech-Language Pathology.* 10(1).

Hoff and Bergler. (2001). The Positive Influence of Dogs on Children in Divorce Crises from the Mother's

Perspective. *Presented at the 9th International Conference on Human-Animal Interactions.* Rio de Janeiro.

Hunt, Hart and Gomulkiewicz. (1992). Role of Small Animals in Social Interactions Between Strangers. *Journal of Social Psychology.* 129

Kelly. (2002). Pet Facilitated Therapy in an Outpatient Setting. *Dissertation Abstracts Interational: Section B: The Sciences and Engineering.* 62(9-B).

Lieber. (2003). Animal-Assisted Therapy for Elementary Students with Emotional or Behavioral Disorders. *Dissertation Abstracts International: Section B: The Sciences and Engineering.* 63(7-A). University Microfilms International, US

Sato, Senjo, Tanaka & Miyazaki. (2003). A case of refractory borderline personality disorder improved with Animal Assisted Therapy. *Seishin Igaku.* 45(6).

Determine The Number Of Possible Clients Suited For AAT

Determining the approximate number of possible clients that are candidates for the animal assisted therapy program allows the creators of the program to accurately assess the needs of a facility and chart an appropriate course.

Knowing the number of candidates for a program can change the scope of the project. If there are initially only a few clients, then the program can start off smaller and grow as the need arises. If there are a large number of candidates, then the program may need to take more time to set up in the start-up period.

It is also important to determine which units the candidate clients reside in. This can change the program's implementation strategy. Are most of the candidates in one unit/house/area? Some mental health facilities are interested in beginning their AAT programs in certain units, then assessing their success before they expand to other units. It simplifies the process of beginning an AAT program to start in one specialty and then expand into other areas. However, if there are potential clients in many different units, an AAT program may want to implement the program in all units where there are clients in need.

Another consideration when deciding what clients would be suited for AAT is what type of therapy will be part of the animal assisted therapy program. Some programs only have counselors in their AAT programs, while other programs involve therapists, psychiatrists, occupational therapists, mental health nurses, etc. There may be clients who would be suitable for occupational therapy AAT but not psychological AAT. Knowing what interventions clients would be suited for can affect the overall number of suitable clients.

The final and most important consideration when calculating the number of suitable clients is the contraindications to animal assisted therapy. Characteristics that would make clients ineligible for AAT include: severe allergies, fear, cultural intolerances of animals, unpredictable violent behavior, and a history of violence towards animals.

A note from a Chimo Project therapist about a history of animal abuse:

> When a client does have a history (or reported history) of animal abuse, the nature of the incident should be investigated. In one training session, it was reported that a client had been 'tagged' as an animal abuser. This client could not be placed in foster homes with animals, and was not allowed to associate with animals. The child and youth care workers who were assigned to this client could not believe that this client was an animal abuser. Upon investigation, it was found that the client (a young girl) had been caught dressing the foster family's cat in doll clothes. The mother told the girl that was animal abuse, and it was noted as such on the client's file. This client should not be removed from an AAT program because of her 'history of animal abuse'. However it is also worthwhile mentioning a situation where a therapist had a client with a history of animal abuse, and the abuse consisted of killing a small dog. So it is important for professional to investigate the nature of a client's history.

The initial list of clients eligible for AAT treatment is meant to be a general one, not a list of names for therapy. Clients come and go from facilities (often between making the list and starting therapy), and the list is meant to be a general guideline to provide those implementing the program with information.

Training The Therapists

Therapist training sessions consisted of five, one-hour sessions, covering:
- An introduction to animal assisted therapy
- A historical overview of animal uses in pet therapy
- Results of the chimo project and other research studies
- Current program and funding
- The difference between AAT, aaa, and pet visitation
- What makes a great therapy animal
- How animals are trained for therapy work
- When is AAT not beneficial?
- Liability issues
- Example AAT applications and techniques
- Developing rapport, fostering relationships, facilitating bonding, addressing emotions, promoting empathy, building self-esteem, promoting 'giving' behavior, providing a sense of control, reducing abusive thoughts and behaviors, addressing anxiety, depression and adhd
- Knowing the therapy animal
- Policies and procedures
- Completing evaluations from each AAT session

Session One
This session is to help therapists gain a basic understanding of the concepts of animal assisted therapy. It includes a general overview of AAT and what will be taught in the five sessions, definitions, brief examples, history, research results and information about the current AAT program. Session One is designed to give the therapists basic information and to inspire excitement about animal assisted therapy.

Session Two
This session is designed to help therapists grasp some of the finer concepts involved in animal assisted therapy. It covers: the difference between Animal Assisted Therapy, Animal

Assisted Activities, and Pet Visitation; what makes a great therapy animal; how animals are tested for therapy work; assessing when AAT is not beneficial; and liability issues surrounding animal assisted therapy work.

Session Three

This session is the basis of the therapist training series and covers how to practice animal assisted therapy with clients. At the beginning of a session it is important for an instructor to talk to the therapists-in-training about the kinds of problems they deal with in their practice, and how they hope to use animal assisted therapy to help them. This understanding will allow the instructor to tailor the session to the training needs of the therapists. Most issues are the same for all groups, but some therapists may have specific therapeutic issues that can be addressed using AAT.

The first issue to be covered in Session Three is how to introduce the therapy animal into the therapy session: how to introduce the animal to the client and how to explain to the client (in age-appropriate language) what the animal is to do in the sessions. If possible introductions should be made outside the therapy room, where there is plenty of personal space for the animal and the client. The client may be asked if they would like to greet the animal and pet it. If these interactions go well, then the client can be asked if they would like to go into the therapy room with the therapist and the animal. Once the animal and the client have settled into the office, then the therapist can explain to the client what the animal will be doing (example):

> *Rupert the cat is a special therapy cat and he helps me talk to people. He is here to make you feel comfortable while we talk today. He loves to be petted and hugged. He likes to play with his springy toys sometimes, and sometimes he just likes to curl up and sleep. He likes people*

like you very much, and it is up to you if you
want to interact with him.

Once the therapists have learned to introduce the animal to the client, then the instructor will encourage the therapists to role play with each other in groups of three (therapist, client, observer) to practice introducing therapy animals. For the role playing, it is preferable for the therapists to be using real animals. If that is not possible, then stuffed animals can be used.

Once the therapists know how to introduce the therapy animals, they need to know what to do with the animal in the therapy session. The first step in this process is pinpointing a client's problem that needs to be addressed. What is the specific problem that the therapist wants to work on in the AAT session? Anxiety? Self-Esteem? Verbalization?

After the therapists isolated the problem to be addressed in the AAT session, they are instructed to set goals for that session with the client. Is the goal to increase assertive behavior? Decrease anxiety? Improve empathy?

Once the therapists can identify problems and set goals for the client in the AAT session, they are trained in the specific techniques and strategies for using the animal to help the client achieve their goals. This is a good time to review the treatment goals and AAT strategies provided in the back of this manual.

This is an area where different types of therapists may have different issues that require a variety of solutions. An occupational therapist may have clients who have problems with sensory integration. The goal here might be improving sensory integration by having the client rub different parts of the dog's body and comment on the different textures of the nose, fur, and foot pads. A psychiatrist may have the goal of accurately diagnosing a new client. In this case, the strategy would be to arrange interactions between the client and the animal, and use the client's reactions to help reach a diagnostic conclusion.

Now that the therapists know how to identify problems, pick goals and decide on AAT strategies, they can put the information together and create session treatment plans using treatment planning worksheets. Once the therapists have completed the worksheets, they are put into groups of three to role play the interaction.

Here is an example:

The Chimo Project: AAT Intervention Planning WORKSHEET

Symptom/ Deficit
Bobby does not trust me (therapist) enough to talk about his problems
Treatment Goal
Develop rapport with the therapist
Treatment Strategy
The animal may be a common interest between the therapist and client and thus can create a bond and foster discussion.
Was the Treatment Successful?
Yes. Bobby and I both owned dogs growing up, and we talked about how much we both loved our dogs. Pippin put his head on Bobby's lap, and we talked about how the therapy dog was different from and similar to our childhood dogs. Bobby was more open to me about his childhood than he has ever been previously.

THERAPY ANIMAL BEHAVIOR INVENTORY			
Therapy Animal Name:	Pippin	**Handler:**	K. Aanderson

BASIC BEHAVIOR (use check mark)			ADVANCED BEHAVIOR	
	Walks politely on leash		Learned new trick	
✓	Recognized client at beginning of the session		Picks up/retrieves objects on command	
Sits/ Stays	On leash	Off leash	Holds objects in mouth	
Downs /Stays	On leash	Off leash	Tugs	
	Did trick for client		Plays fetch/plays with toy	
✓	Comes/sits next to person (off leash)	✓	Empathetic Response	
✓	Sits/lies/stays with client for petting	✓	Sits/lies/stays with client without petting	
	Brushed by client		Made a mistake (client frustrated or handler corrected humanely)	
✓	Took treat from client		Other:	

For more information about using animals in counseling sessions, please read Dr. Cynthia Chandler's book *Animal Assisted Therapy in Counseling.*

Session Four
This session is dedicated totally to learning about the nature of the therapy animal. Therapists learn the meaning of body postures, the causes of stress and how to recognize stress in an animal, problem/ unacceptable behaviors, zoonoses and infection control, proper equipment for a therapy session, how to prevent accidents and

injuries, and how to be on the lookout for hazards to the animal's welfare.

Session Five
The final sets of topics covered in these training sessions are the policies and procedures surrounding animal assisted therapy at their facility and evaluation measures. These items will be different for every facility that AAT operates in and dictated by the unique situation of each location. The policies and procedures often include: animal supervision, routes to be taken to and from therapy sessions, suitable areas for the animals to exercise/eliminate, infection control measures, accident clean-up, incident reporting, off-limits areas, animal handler responsibilities, and therapist responsibilities. For more information about what is included in this section, please see the section titled Drafting Policy and Procedure in this manual.

In order to be classified as animal assisted therapy, the therapy sessions must be monitored and the client's progress tracked. Therapists are introduced to the AAT evaluation forms included in the appendix of this manual and instructed on how to complete them. They are then informed about how the results are used to track the progress of individual clients and the AAT program at the facility.

Near the end of Session Five, an 'ad-hoc' test of the therapists' knowledge is advisable. This allows the instructor to spot any gaps in their knowledge and to reiterate the missed information or clear up confusion.

If an instructor is able to bring a therapy dog to the training sessions, then they should purposefully do some things wrong and some right with the animal. The therapists should be asked to try and spot the correct and incorrect animal handling procedures. Some examples of handler errors are: forgetting to bring the animal's water dish, having the animal wearing the wrong collar, and allowing the animal to rush up to the therapists at the beginning of the session. The instructor should make notes about what they have intentionally done correctly and incorrectly, and see how many items the therapists are able to point out. The instructor may be surprised by some things they might be doing -wrong or right- that they didn't even think of.

After the quick animal handling 'test', the therapists should again form groups of three to do one last role playing, utilizing everything they have learned in the five sessions. At the beginning of the session, the therapists complete the intervention planning worksheet, and at the end of the session they complete the evaluation form. After this role playing is complete, the therapists are brought back into a group and talk about how the role playing went, what they learned, what they think they will take forward, and if they had any problems or questions.

After these training sessions, the therapists should be able to successfully use animal assisted therapy with their clients.

Deciding Staff Animals Or Volunteer Animals

When beginning an animal assisted therapy program, it is important to decide where the animals will be recruited from. Using animals belonging to therapists/staff or volunteers each presents pros and cons. None of the difficulties are insurmountable, just points to consider when setting up a program.

Staff Animals	Volunteer Animals
PROS Available all hours that the staff member is working Reliability – less chance of cancellation Can be a last minute replacement if another therapy animal is unable to attend a session	**PROS** Someone whose only responsibility is the well being of the animal Bridges the gap between the general public and those with mental illness Can assist therapy work with any trained therapist Additional input on therapy process. Another set of eyes and ears in sessions. Handlers care for the animal outside the session (travel, pee breaks, etc.), so staff do not incur any additional demands on their time outside the actual therapy session Generally will not approach a program unless they have companion animals they believe capable of passing the tests

Staff Animals	Volunteer Animals
CONS	**CONS**
Must find staff members/ therapists who have a suitable therapy animal and take it through the training procedures	Handlers must incur costs associated with AAT program (vet, travel, training, testing, etc.) which could ultimately drive them away from the program
Staff member must care for the animal as well as perform their normal jobs	Often has other commitments/not available from 9-5
In sessions, the therapist must function as both therapist and animal handler, resulting in possible split attention	Can leave the program due to life events
No additional input from another perspective	Another person in the therapy session (although research does not indicate that this is a problem)
Staff member must find ways to provide the animal with time away from therapy sessions	Requires more paperwork and procedure
Interested staff members may not have animals	Difficult to recruit suitable animals and handlers
Interested staff members may have animals that are not able to pass the basic tests required to become a therapy animal, resulting in disappointment and possible departure from the AAT program	
Animal can work only with its staff member handler	

Determining If Therapists/Staff Are Interested In Training Their Own Pets

If the facility has determined that it would like to pursue the option of therapists using their own animal friends as therapy animals, the next step is to determine which therapists are interested. An information sheet and a questionnaire can be circulated to staff at the facility to determine the feasibility of this option.

The information sheet should include the certification procedure for the animals and the therapists, how animal assisted therapy will be used at the facility, what animals are eligible for the program, and the options for caring for their animals on site.
The questionnaire should elicit information about the therapists', what types of animals they have that they believe may be suitable for therapy work, what training/ temperament those animals have, where they would like the animals to be housed on site, what special equipment/ considerations they may need to care for their animals on site, how long the therapists believe they would need to care for their animal friends each day, how the animal would arrive at the therapy site, and why they are interested in using their pets as therapy animals. A sample, questionnaire can be found in the appendix of this manual.
The answers to these questions can help programs decide if having therapists/staff use their own animals would be a suitable option for the site as well as how to best care for those animals.

It is essential that the therapists using their own animal friends as therapy animals is presented separately from the issue of therapists becoming involved with the animal assisted therapy program. Many talented, enthusiastic therapists may feel like they cannot be part of the program because they do not own a suitable therapy animal. A program should also have a plan in place to deal with the inevitable disappointment if a staff member's animal that does not pass the rigorous screening procedures. The therapists should be reminded that there are a wide variety of alternatives when considering how to use animals in a facility. It is vital, when running an animal assisted therapy program, that everyone feels that they are able to contribute to the success of the program.

Drafting A Work Plan

When implementing an animal assisted therapy program at a facility, it is vitally important that a formal work plan is put in place before any work begins. There are simply too many people and variables involved for those implementing the program to not to have the plan recorded.

Creating a successful AAT program requires a number of steps to be completed long before an animal every puts a paw in a facility. All of these points should be outlined on a work plan which includes target completion dates.

First, establish a general direction for the AAT program.
>Will therapists be using their own pets or will volunteer handler teams be needed?
>Which therapists in what treatments will be involved?

Second, policies and procedures must be created to help guide the general direction of the program.
>What is the purpose of AAT at the facility?
>Where will the animals be allowed?
>How long can they be in the facility?
>What training do therapists need to practice AAT?
>How will allergies be dealt with?

Third, an evaluation plan should be created to check the progress of the AAT program once it is up and running including program, therapist, and client outcome evaluations.

Fourth, therapists and animals must be recruited and trained to be part of the program.

Finally, everyone who will be involved with the program should be consulted one final time to ensure that all the variables involved in the program have been agreed upon. Then let the therapy begin!

Example Work Plan for Implementation of Animal-Assisted Therapy

**Work plans may vary depending on the therapist's schedule,
so these plans must be flexible**

Target Date	Activity
Jan 5-30	Recruit and screen potential volunteers who have appropriate animals for the youth to work with in the classrooms or houses. Draft necessary risk-management policies and procedures. Review AAT questionnaires and choose appropriate questions to ask at weekly check-ins.
Week of Jan 26	Establish plans for consistent recording of information to be used in the evaluation of AAT (e.g., daily progress notes, <u>tracking individual choices for "feeling faces"</u>, tracking reward choices). Review and finalize the evaluation plan.
Week of Feb 2	Start working with animal in designated classrooms on a regular basis (e.g. three days per week). Submit AAT program implementation information and the evaluation plan to Children's Services. Begin monitoring the progress of youths receiving AAT.
Week of Feb 9	Prepare a press release/conference to announce the project. Begin planning for news conference in March.
Week of Feb 16	Begin regular evening activities with animals in designated houses.
Week of Mar 8	Begin collecting and analyzing evaluation information collected to date.

	Hold news conference with Minister of Children's Services.
Week of Mar 15	Hold focus group with youth in classroom and houses participating in AAT to obtain their perspectives. Interview staff and parents about their satisfaction with the AAT program.
Week of Mar 22	Collect remaining evaluation information.
Week of Mar 29	Prepare an evaluation report to summarize the implementation of the AAT program.

Preparing An Evaluation Plan

When implementing an AAT program at a facility, it is essential to know what is working and what is not. Evaluations are a critical aspect of animal assisted therapy that differentiates it from other types of pet therapy. These evaluations are vital for a program to learn and grow as it progresses. When practicing AAT, there are three types of evaluations; client, therapist, and program.

Client Evaluations
One of the features of animal assisted therapy is that the client's progress is evaluated on an ongoing basis. In order to track a client's progress in therapy, it is necessary to create an evaluation tool that measures the program's intended outcomes. This measure should ideally be used after every AAT session. The outcome measure should include variables such as previous/current pet ownership, an overall assessment (does the animal help you at school, at home, in social situations?), and a personal assessment of the animal's effect (does the animal help you feel good about yourself? Can you focus better when the animal is there? Is it easier to talk when the animal is there?). If volunteer handlers are being used, then should be included questions regarding the effect of having the handler in the therapy session.

The importance of an evaluation tool being written/presented in developmentally age appropriate language cannot be stressed enough. Suffers of FASD often are developmentally delayed and may need the questions to be presented in extremely plain/simple language and pictures may be needed in order to ensure that the client understands the questions being asked of them. Terms such as *concentrate, attention, comfortable, assigned, complete,* and *questionnaire* may be too complicated for some clients with FASD. Better choices of words would be *think, feel better, jobs, do, test,* etc. It is also imperative that the evaluation be as short as possible.

One symptom of FASD is difficulty concentrating. Completing the evaluation measure should not become another therapy exercise. Clients not being able to understand the questions or becoming frustrated when completing the questionnaire can negatively affect the results being reported and make the evaluations pointless. Taking a little extra time and using a little creativity on the evaluation can make all the difference in the results obtained.

A short sample evaluation for young children suffering from FASD appears on the next page:

Help Scruffy and friends do this test!

Scruffy has to help you with these questions before he can have his bone!	
Scruffy has to help you with these questions before he can have his bone!	**Circle the picture that is like how you feel.**
1. The therapy animal helps me feel good about myself.	Not at all A Lot
2. It was easier to talk when the therapy animal is here.	Not at all A Lot
3. The therapy animal helps me feel okay with my therapist.	Not at all A Lot
Almost there! 4. I can think better when the therapy animal is here.	Not at all A Lot
Scruffy says Thanks for helping him!	

A full client evaluation questionnaire for general populations with FASD is included in the appendix of this manual.

Therapist evaluations
It is important to have the therapists complete evaluations on the progress of their clients in the animal assisted therapy program. These questionnaires ask the therapists to objectively describe their client's behavior in AAT sessions and to make educated guesses about the client's feelings and thoughts during and after the AAT sessions.

Although complicated word comprehension is not a concern with therapists, the length and flow of the questionnaire is. Therapists are already using up extra time to schedule and perform the AAT session, so completing a questionnaire represents an additional burden. A well-constructed questionnaire can be longer than a choppy, confusing one and still be measurable. However, the longer and more complicated a questionnaire is, the less chance there is of having the therapist fill them out. Even if they do complete the questionnaire, a therapist may rush through and not pause to reflect on the responses they are giving. Ideally, therapists would complete one questionnaire per client, per session, so a program should investigate every possibility to streamline the outcome questionnaire procedure. These steps may include: allowing therapists to complete the forms on a computer and email the responses to the program, having the identification portions of the questionnaires already completed, or finding ways to shorten the questionnaire.

A sample therapist questionnaire is included in the appendix of this manual.

Program evaluations
It is important that the program itself is subject to separate evaluations. Program evaluation plans should resemble work plans, with specific tasks and deadlines, but pertain to the continuing operation of the animal assisted therapy program.

The four areas needed in an evaluation plan are:

Areas of inquiry – What are the specific things being evaluated?

Indicators – How is it determined if those specific things have been achieved?

Evaluation activities, data source and method – What are the specific ways used to measure the achievement of tasks?

Timeline – How often will these items be evaluated what is the deadline for completion of these activities?

The four areas are filled in with specific tasks for completing the program evaluation. Tasks can be completed on a weekly, monthly, or bi-monthly basis. Tasks on the evaluation plan should include: how much service did the AAT program provide? Who received service? What are the outcomes you are hoping for? Are the people interacting with the AAT program satisfied? The final step is preparation of a report on the AAT program.

The completion of a program evaluation plan, makes it easier to see the strengths and weaknesses in the animal assisted therapy program. Efforts can then be made to emphasize the strengths and address the weaknesses.

Example Evaluation Plan For Animal-Assisted Therapy

Evaluation plans may vary depending on the therapist's schedule, so these plans must be flexible

Area of Inquiry and/or Initiative	Indicators	Evaluation Activities, Data Source and Method	Timeline
How much service did the AAT program provide?	• Number of children admitted, treated and discharged • Average length of time youths received AAT	Compile information from Bosco client database and records.	Entire program duration
Who receives service?	• Age • Gender • Residence location • Bosco House and Classroom • Presenting concern or diagnosis • Number of diagnoses	Describe population who received services, using information from the database and/or health records.	As above
What are the short-term outcomes of service?	Academic ability and achievement	Compile pre/post WIAT scores for youths who received AAT.	Admission & discharge (or at 4 mon. after admission)
	Teacher assessment of classroom dynamics	Review and summarize subjective opinions of classroom functioning that teachers record in their daily progress reports.	Entire Program
	Impact on behavior	Review and count critical incidents reports from the classroom and house. Compare to baseline numbers from a comparable period.	As above

Area of Inquiry and/or Initiative	Indicators	Evaluation Activities, Data Source and Method	Timeline
	Impact on emotions and feelings	Review and summarize subjective ratings of feelings of youths. Teachers document which "feeling faces" the youths chose each day and note which days an animal was present.	Daily logs from first two mon. then review feasibility of continuation
	Attitude towards staff	Review and summarize AAT questionnaires completed by youth at their house check-ins.	Weekly for first two mon. then review as above to determine frequency
	Attitude towards working with an animal	Review and summarize AAT questionnaires completed by youth at their house check-ins. Track and summarize the number of times the animal is chosen for the reward activity in the classroom.	Weekly for first two months, then review as above
	Progress towards goals	Therapists and youth will rate the youths' progress towards their goals at the weekly check-ins. Review and summarize weekly progress and take note of the involvement of the animal with each youth.	Weekly for entire program duration
Are people who interact with AAT program satisfied?	Client satisfaction	Hold a focus group with youth in each classroom and house who participated in AAT, and summarize their perspectives.	Bi-yearly for program duration

Area of Inquiry and/or Initiative	Indicators	Evaluation Activities, Data Source and Method	Timeline
	Parent satisfaction	Develop, administer, and summarize results from a parent's telephone questionnaire.	As above
	Staff satisfaction	Develop, administer, and summarize responses from a staff questionnaire	As above
Preparation of reports		Evaluation of program implementation	Two mon. after program begins
		First-year evaluation results	End of yr. 1
		Second-year evaluation results	End of yr. 1
		Final report	End of yr. 2

Chapter 3: Animals and Volunteers

Understanding The Animal In Therapy
Sessions

Creating An Animal-Safe Environment

Determining Staff Animal Needs

The 'Doggie' Bag

Obedience Testing

Small Animal Obedience Testing

Temperament Testing

Health Screening

Volunteer Recruitment

Volunteer Screening

Volunteer Orientation/Training

Matching Volunteers With Facilities/Therapists

Volunteer Retention

Facility Orientation For Volunteers

Boundaries For Volunteers

Understanding The Animal In Therapy Sessions

It is important for everyone involved in animal assisted therapy programs to be familiar with the basics of animal behavior. Knowing why the animal is acting the way it is can prevent unwanted situations from arising. Therapy work may look simple, but it can be taxing for the therapy animal. It is possible to 'sour' an animal to therapy work by ignoring their signals that they need to rest, for example:

Basic Behaviors
There are five basic sets of animal behavior: relaxation, disinterest, arousal, fear, and aggression. Most often, therapy animals are relaxed, but it is important to know the signs indicating when they are not relaxed, and what needs to be done.

Disinterest	*Arousal or interest*
No eye contact	Hackles up at shoulders only
Turns away	Ears alert, moving
Trying to leave	Face alert
Sniffing Excessively	Posture forward
Yawning Excessively	Minimal vocalizations
➢ This can indicate that the animal needs a break from the session	➢ This is a transitional stage. The dog will move to a different posture and/or emotion.
Fear	*Aggression*
Dilated pupils	• Hackles up to the shoulders and hips only
Ears back	• Growling – deep, belly growl
Tight face	• Nothing about the animal is relaxed
Panting	• Direct, fixed stare
Hackles all the way up the back	• Erect, forward posture
➢ Find out what is causing the reaction, and either remove	• Tight mouth

the fear-inducing element, or remove the animal from the situation	• Volley of vocalizations ➢ Remove the animal from the situation immediately

Stress

It is important to recognize signs of stress in a dog, especially while he is participating in animal-assisted therapy. His 'work' may be tiring and stressful, and it is the handler's responsibility to be able to recognize when the animal needs a break.

Some signs of stress in animals include:
• shaking
• excessive dandruff
• dilated pupils
• excessive blinking
• piloerection
• loss of appetite (refusing a treat)
• sudden onset of excessive shedding
• diarrhea
• yawning
• sniffing
• licking lips
• scratching
• restlessness, distraction, agitation
• sweating through the pads of the feet
• inappropriate urination/defecation
• 'shutting down' by turning away or avoiding eye contact
• shyness, reluctance to approach people
• increased activity or pacing
• panting and salivating
• whining, excessive vocalizing
• hiding behind the handler
• need for repeated commands

In times of stress, instinct often prevails over training, it is important to take steps to eliminate stress before the animal is in the session, and do everything possible to minimize stressful elements.

Causes of stress in animals
Every animal reacts differently to its environment. Some of the more common stressors for dogs in animal-assisted therapy programs include:
- Unusual noises
- Unknown places
- Confusing or inconsistent training or handling
- Rough or unpredictable handling
- Crowding by people
- People exhibiting inappropriate or unusual behaviors
- Unusual smells
- Unusual emotional reactions of the handler
- Extreme temperatures (outside and inside)

Anything new, unfamiliar, or out of the ordinary can be perceived as dangerous and may result in stress-related behaviors.

Creating an Animal-Safe Environment

Facilities should recognize some of the risks that animals may be exposed to in an animal-assisted therapy program and consider how to best protect their safety and welfare.

Preventing Accidents and Injuries

Most potential accidents and injuries can be prevented with a little preparation and forethought. Some general guidelines for safe human-animal interaction include:

- Only health-screened and behavior-assessed companion animals should be used in animal-assisted therapy programs;
- Never encourage or permit an animal to be left unattended with a client.
- An animal should never be tied to furniture.
- The collar, leash, etc., should be appropriate for the therapy animal and should aid the handler in working with the animal. Prong collars, head halters, and other training devices should not be necessary on a companion animal that is appropriate for an animal-assisted therapy program. Prong collars also present a risk if a client's hand comes in contact with the prongs. A flexi-lead may maximize the handler's distance from the dog, increasing the risk of accidents. As well, a flexi-lead can injure an animal, or even a person, if it is dropped or pulled from a handler's hand.
- Animals should never be placed in a potentially dangerous situation or asked to engage in an activity that is deemed unsafe

Possible hazards for therapy animals

Aggressive Behavior
Clients with unpredictable or aggressive behavior should be identified and monitored to protect the animal from rough handling or injury.

Medication
A careful visual check of the floor, client's pockets, tabletops, etc., will ensure that no medication is accessible to the therapy animal.

Hazardous Materials
Ensure that all hazardous materials (cleaners, chemical, poisons, etc.) are properly stored and not accessible -- a good idea for client safety as well as that of the therapy animal.
Pest control poison is a major concern for animal safety, not only if the animal comes into contact directly with the poison, but also through contact with an animal that has ingested the poison.

Drinking Water
Ensure there is fresh drinking water available and a safe place for the animal to eliminate.

Excessive Treats
Do not encourage or permit over-feeding of treats.

Excessive Heat

Be willing to modify or even cancel an animal-assisted therapy session if the temperature is hot. It is hard on the animal, and hot weather can affect a dog's personality making them irritable and more easily stressed.

Overwork

When seeing the positive results of animal assisted therapy, it is natural to want *everyone* to receive the benefits. However, this may not be beneficial to the animal, and the last thing that any handler would want is to 'sour' their animal on therapy work due to overuse. It may look like the animal is just 'lazing around', but therapy work is stressful for even the most laid back animal. It is recommended that therapy animals do no more than one hour of therapy work before a substantial break. The length of the break and the length and number of sessions depends on the animal.

Determining Staff Animal Needs

Once a facility has determined that staff animals will be used in the animal assisted therapy program, it is necessary to determine the needs of the animals. Animal safety should always be the first consideration. Factors include heat or cold, other animals, and poisons/chemicals.

The first step is to determine the types of staff and volunteer animals that will be used at the facility. If a facility is utilizing only dogs, then their requirements will be different from a program that uses dogs, cats and rabbits. Knowing what kinds of animals will be used at the facility affects the overall makeup of the animal care package required.

It is important to determine if the animals are able to interact with each other (e.g., dogs) or must be kept away from one another (e.g., a greyhound and a therapy rabbit).

Once it has been established what types of animals will be used, it should be considered how long the animals will be at the facility in a given work week. Resident animals will have different needs than animals who are present only for a one-hour therapy session, then leave the facility. Assessing the length of time the animals will be at the facility affects planning with regard to infrastructure, management, and the handlers themselves. If animals are to be present for long periods of time, plans need to be made for safe exercise areas, places to eliminate, and the provision of food, water, and toys or treats for the animals. Regardless of how long the animals are at the facility, there should always be a kennel, cat tree, or rabbit hutch that the animal can retreat to during therapy sessions that become too stressful.

It is also important to recognize that staff members may have their own considerations when dealing with their animals' needs. A solution that works for dogs in general, may not work for a particular staff member's animal. In these situations, the staff member should be asked how they would like to accommodate their animal's needs, and be provided with the necessary support.

By planning ahead, it is possible for an animal assisted therapy program to use staff animals with great success.

A survey to determine staff animal needs is included in the appendix of this manual.

The 'Doggie' Bag

All animal handlers should have this bag with them at all times. This bag should contain everything that the animal may need before, during, or after their sessions.

It is recommended that the handler use a backpack or 'sling' backpack for this bag. When handling an animal, they are easier to manage than an over-the-shoulder bag.

This bag should contain:

- hand sanitizer
- the animal's therapy animal ID tag or bandana (this should be put on when entering the facility)
- the animal's special therapy collar with a quick-release catch (this should be put on before the visit)
- the animal's normal collar
- a second leash
- water dish
- water bottle with water from home (some animals can be picky about water)
- hand towel for cleaning muddy feet, drool, spilled water from dish, etc.
- large bath sheet (towel) to place over client's lap if the animal is leaning on them or sitting in their lap
- treats
- toys (ball, tug rope, cat feather toys, etc.)
- pen and paper
- a large zip-lock bag with:
  - paper towels
  - plastic bags for pickup duties
- pictures of your pet to give to clients (optional)
- anything else you think your pet might need

Obedience Testing

It is mandatory in almost all pet therapy programs for animals to be required to complete some form of obedience testing, and it is strongly recommended by the authors of this manual. A test to determine the obedience of a potential therapy animal is important, but the issue of **how** to test for obedience can become complicated.

For liability and reliability purposes, it would be optimal to require high levels of obedience from therapy animals. An excellent test for this would be the national kennel club's obedience testing. These tests are standardized, they often represent the national standard of obedience, and the logistics are dealt with because the tests are run entirely by the breed organizations. They also offer programs limited liability protection, since it can be indicated that a program did everything possible to screen out animal candidates that may cause a negative incident.

However, many of the items on these tests run contrary to the important qualities of a good therapy animal. There are test items such as 'accept the approach of the friendly stranger' where the evaluator approaches the handler, and the animal cannot initiate contact. While this is an important obedience exercise, one of the most valuable qualities of a therapy animal is the willingness to initiate contact with the clients in therapy. Many of the good qualities of a therapy animal would result in an animal failing item on standard obedience tests. Perfect therapy animals with total obedience and the natural behaviors that make them excellent in the therapy session are rare. Because most therapy animals have not been bred, raised, and trained their whole lives to be therapy animals, most are just happy to be there.

Kennel club obedience tests also do not award points for enthusiasm displayed by the dog and the handler. One of the most important criteria for selecting an animal, as well as a handler, is their attitude. Most kennel club tests also do not dock points for stern handling of the animal. Rough handling (including 'popping' the leash) is not welcome in mental health animal therapy work. Many clients involved with animal assisted therapy have a history of being abused or witnessing abusive behavior. It would be extremely detrimental for these individuals to be exposed to rough methods of handling the animals. A mental health AAT program may need to address the issues of rough handling by the handler if the program uses a kennel club type of obedience test.

The occurrence of the test should also be a consideration. Obedience tests run by kennel clubs often occur on a fixed schedule (sometimes quite seldom) and have a small pool of trained evaluators. If volunteers have to wait upwards of a month for a testing time, many of them will lose interest and leave the program.

There is also the issue of breed/animal specific concerns that must be addressed. Many official obedience tests will not make breed specific exceptions to their tests. Sitting is an extremely uncomfortable pose for Greyhounds, and many will not do it because of the pain it causes them. Some older pets would make excellent 'lap warmer' therapy animals, but they certainly would not pass a standard obedience test.
In addition, countless potential handlers are hesitant with the perceived amount of work involved in preparing a dog for a kennel club obedience test. There is a considerable amount of work involved with preparing a therapy animal for rigorous obedience testing, and many handlers are willing to work in therapy sessions, but not to spend weeks or months training their dog to high levels of obedience.

To avoid many of these concerns, it is possible for programs to find a good animal trainer in their area and create their own obedience test. The concern with this is the standards of the test (are they stringent enough?) and liability concerns. This test also may not be valid if the handler wished to pursue animal therapy elsewhere. A program must therefore decide what is important and how to evaluate their criteria for acceptable therapy animals. When deciding what type of obedience test to use, a program must balance liability protection, positive therapy animal (and handler) qualities, evaluator availability, the ability to make breed/animal specific allowances, and volunteer willingness.

Both The Chimo Project's Pet Therapy Obedience Test and the Canine Good Neighbor Test are available in the appendix of this manual.

Small Animal Obedience Testing

Testing the obedience of small animals can be a tricky issue. How do you test the obedience of small animals? Does the cat have to perform a heeling pattern?

In the past, various organizations have offered a Feline Good Neighbor Test. Generally, any modified version of the obedience test will be acceptable. There are many exercises that small animals are not required to perform, such as, 'come when called'. However, many of the exercises from standard obedience tests can be adapted to small animals.

Accepting petting, being carried while the handler walks (instead of heeling), and demonstrating calm reactions to distractions are all important obedience tests for small animals.

A copy of the Small Animal Obedience Test can be found in the appendix of this manual.

Temperament Testing

"The handler volunteers, but the animal gets recruited."
A quote from a training session at the Northern Alberta Pet Therapy Society's training.

It important that prospective therapy animals complete temperament testing to evaluate their suitability for work in animal assisted therapy. Some animals are just not comfortable performing AAT. Most companion animals will do things because you ask them to, but if they do not enjoy what they are doing, it is unfair to expect them to continue.

Temperament testing evaluates whether or not the animal will be suitable for and enjoy therapy work. An animal may be wonderful in predictable circumstances - at home and with people they know. However, to be a good therapy animal they must display those same characteristics in unfamiliar situations.

The elements in this test are designed to replicate the situation that the animals are likely to encounter when in a therapy session. The requirements for dogs, cats, and small animals are similar because the situations they will be placed in are essentially the same.

For testing, the animal should be taken into an unfamiliar setting and tested by a stranger with the handler present.
1. Petted and examined (in ears and eyes) by stranger
2. Exuberant or clumsy petting
3. Reaction to movement
4. Restraining hug
5. Staggering/ Gesturing individual
6. Yelling
7. Response to a light tug on the fur
8. Direct stare, blow in the face
9. Bumped from behind

10. Crowded and petted by several people
11. Sit with stranger
12. Take a treat
13. Free play

A more elaborate description of these exercises in available in the index of this manual.

Testing for appropriate temperament in a therapy animal protects both the welfare of the animal and the safety of the people who will be interacting with it.

Health Screening

It is necessary to do everything possible to maintain the health of those involved with animal assisted therapy including clients, handlers, therapists, and animals. Before being certified for therapy work all animals should undergo a health check by a veterinarian, which includes the general condition of the animal, vital signs, physical appearance, fecal test, a check for parasites, and an updated immunization or titer test. A titer test is a blood test that checks the levels of an animal's immunity to disease, and that can replace annual vaccinations.

Examples of dog and cat health screenings are available in the appendix of this manual.

Zoonoses and Infection Control
Zoonoses are infectious diseases which are transmitted from vertebrate animals to human beings. Types of transmission include direct contact with animal; contact with an infected animal, its feces or living environment; bite or scratch incident; or inhalation.
Zoonoses include rabies, salmonellosis, campylobateriosis, streptococcal infections, and giardiasis.

In order to reduce the risk of transmission:
- A regular vaccination and parasite prevention schedule should be maintained.
- Contact with wild animals should be avoided.
- Animal's feces in public areas and yard or litter box/pan should be cleaned up.
- Fleas and skin problems should be checked for by running hands through the animal's coat on a regular basis.
- Dog should be feed fresh, nutritious food from clean dishes and have fresh water in a clean bowl available.
- The animal should not be allowed to drink from the toilet.
- Good personal hygiene, including hand washing, should be practiced.

- The therapy animal should not be used if there is any possibility that the animal is not well.

With these safeguards in place, The Chimo Project has not had a single negative experience in its seven years of operation.

Volunteer Recruitment

The need for trained therapy animals in your animal assisted therapy program can be addressed by using volunteers in the community. It is a good idea to look at the population of volunteers you would like to have, then to target them in your recruitment. Do you want mainly retired volunteers with their free time? University students? Kennel Club members? Once you have a general idea of where you would like to focus your recruitment efforts, you can then determine how to recruit. A program can use many avenues such as advertising, meet and greets, and word of mouth.

Advertising
There are a variety of media that will advertise your need for volunteers and their animal friends. Local newspapers, pet magazines, animal shelters, breed rescue associations, pet stores, off leash parks, obedience schools, kennel clubs, radio talk shows, television, and internet websites are usually available or willing to help non-profit organizations. Creating your own website also helps to raise the profile of your program and recruit volunteers.

Meet and Greet
By going to Kennel Club shows, Pet Expos or Dog Jogs you raise the profile of your AAT program and may find volunteers who are interested in being part of your program. Going out into the community offers the opportunity to achieve there these two objectives at once. 'Meet and greets' also give potential volunteers time to ask questions, and give you the opportunity to sell them on the benefits of volunteering. A person who would not have answered a newspaper ad may be willing to volunteer after they find out more information about your program.

Word of Mouth

Many people begin volunteering with an organization because they have heard how much their friends were enjoying it. Encourage your volunteers to spread the word to their friends, family, and co-workers.

Volunteer Screening

In order to protect the facility, the staff members, and the clients, faculties require that all volunteers be screened before they begin their work. These screening measures often include items such as reference checks, a resume, background checks, child welfare checks, health screenings, and oaths of confidentiality. If a facility already has a volunteer screening procedure in place, then an animal assisted therapy program should adapt themselves to work within that procedure. At some facilities it is possible for the volunteer screening procedure to be conducted by the volunteer coordinator.

This procedure can be daunting, if not intimidating, to some volunteers. Many volunteers want to begin AAT right away and become frustrated at the multi-step procedure that some facilities have in place. Having a straightforward, streamlined process for volunteers to complete this screening helps ensure that the volunteers will not become discouraged and leave the program. It is also worthwhile for a facility to make a volunteer screening checklist so that volunteers can see all the steps in the program and track their own progress. Regular check-ups on the volunteer's progress also helps them move through the process.

Volunteer Orientation/Training

Having well-trained volunteers is a necessity for any animal assisted therapy program. A happy, well-trained volunteer will be a valued member of the therapeutic team, a lookout for safety issues, and an advocate for the program.

Before beginning work at a facility a volunteer should know:
- *What is Animal Assisted Therapy and what will be expected of them in sessions*
  - What is the program they are involved with?
  - What is animal assisted therapy vs. animal assisted activities or pet visitation?
  - What are the benefits of AAT?
  - When is AAT not beneficial?
  - What happens in an AAT session?
- *Details about the facility they will be volunteering in*
  - Where is it?
  - What is the facility's policy about AAT?
  - Where can the animal eliminate or exercise?
  - Where will the AAT sessions be held?
  - Is there any specific procedure for entering the building and getting to the therapy room?
  - What should they do if there is an incident?
  - Which type of therapist will they be working with?
  - What kind of client will they be working with?
  - On average, how long will the sessions be?
- *What makes a successful AAT volunteer*
  - Example goals and strategies that the therapist may use
  - Details about questionnaires and documentation
  - Self-care
  - Trouble-shooting "My dog has to go to the bathroom." Innovative ways out of sticky situations

- o What support and supervision is available when they are on site and also when they are away from the facility?
- *Issues concerning the companion animal*
  - o Recognizing stress and its causes
  - o Health and welfare
  - o Addressing positive and negative behaviors during an AAT visit
  - o Equipment – the real doggie bag
- *Liability issues*
  - o Whose insurance covers what?
  - o How to avoid liability problems
- *Details about volunteer consent and confidentiality agreements*

Matching Volunteers With Facilities/Therapists

Once a volunteer has completed all the steps required to become a certified animal assisted therapy volunteer with their pet, congratulate them on their progress.

Finally, it is time to match up the volunteer and their animals with an appropriate facility/therapist/program. It is important to match the qualities of the handler and the animal to the needs of the program.

The availability of the handler will often affect their placement. Many therapists work from 8-4 and many volunteers work regular jobs from 9-5. This scheduling conflict may require a volunteer to be matched with a child and youth care worker who works a night shift, or a mental health nurse who works weekends.

The handler's preference should also affect their placement. Some volunteers have a strong desire to work with certain populations, and this desire should be obliged; a volunteer who is excited about their placement is a volunteer who may become a dedicated, long-term volunteer.

The size and temperament of the animals can also affect the placement of a volunteer handler team. A large dog may be better suited for working with troubled youth or very young children who may play rough with the animal, whereas a fragile small dog or cat may be best placed with clients who are able to be gentle with a small animal. The animal's temperament also plays an important role. A sedate cat who likes to sit on a client's lap may be better matched with introverted, shy clients, or one-on-one therapy, whereas an energetic, tennis-ball loving Labrador retriever may be best suited to a recreational group therapy session.

All of these factors are just issues to bear in mind when considering a match between handler, animal and facility. Some cats or small dogs love working with young children, and some large, energetic dogs excel at quietly comforting clients. It is not possible to forecast which animal will be the perfect match for a given program; it is only possible to make an educated guess based on the information at hand. As a program, it is important to be open to placement feedback once a match has been made and make the necessary changes or try another placement in order to create the optimal situation.

Most programs find that animals shine in therapy sessions regardless of the program they are placed in.

Volunteer Retention

Once someone has made the effort to volunteer at a facility, it is of vital importance that such a volunteer be retained. Keeping volunteers happy requires a few simple steps and some creative thinking. It is important for the volunteers to feel that they are making a significant contribution to the community. There are a number of things an organization can do to make their volunteers feel valued, including:

- Personally call to check up on each volunteer once a month. This helps the volunteer to feel cared for, and also enables the program manager to be aware of any concerns the volunteer may have before they become serious issues.
- Document the volunteer's time in a log book. When a pre-determined number of AAT hours or sessions have been achieved, recognize the contribution with a certificate, a t-shirt, or gift certificate.
- Provide the volunteers with positive therapist and client evaluations with client identification removed. This allows the volunteer to see the direct impact their work is having.
- Encourage the therapists to meet briefly with the volunteers after each session for an informal discussion where the therapists can let the volunteer know how the session went, what went well and, what could be improved.
- Have an AAT networking social. An opportunity to meet at a restaurant or a picnic in a dog-friendly park provides the volunteers and therapists an opportunity to meet with each other and discuss their work. It also provides an occasion for the facility to commend the volunteers on their work.

There are other creative things that an organization can do to recognize and reward their volunteers. Sending the therapy animals cards or presents on their birthdays makes the handlers feel that not only they, but also their animal companions are being recognized. Press releases or media events that feature the volunteers and their animals are also excellent sources of recognition.

The retention of volunteers is important when running an animal assisted therapy program at a facility. With a little work and a lot of creativity a facility can keep volunteers happy and committed.

Facility Orientation For Volunteers

Once a volunteer has been matched with a therapy program and therapist, it is necessary for this person to become acquainted with the facility, its policies, the therapist, and the types of clients they will be working with. Often the volunteer coordinators at a facility can complete the on-site orientation for a volunteer handler. When introducing a volunteer handler team to a facility, there are some important facts to keep in mind:

- All involved staff at a facility should be trained and prepared to begin animal assisted therapy before a volunteer team is introduced to a facility.
- Volunteers should be introduced to everyone who they will be involved in the animal assisted therapy program, including the person who will serve as their supervisor (often the AAT program manager).
- The volunteer should be shown where they can park, where the animals can exercise and eliminate, the route they will take into the facility, the room where therapy will be taking place, the areas where therapy animals are allowed and not allowed on-site.
- The therapist should discuss the client treatment plans, emphasizing how the animal will be used in the session.
- The volunteer should be able to express their expectations for how they will be involved.
- If possible, the volunteer should be introduced to the client or types of clients they will be seeing in therapy sessions.

An introductory meeting gives everyone involved an opportunity to get to know each other and to communicate their expectations about the animal assisted therapy program. It also provides an opportunity for the volunteer and the animal to become comfortable with the facility and staff before beginning therapy work.

Boundaries for volunteers

Volunteers are often unsure about how to proceed regarding the boundary issues that are involved in their participation with an animal assisted therapy session. Volunteers often have not received the formalized training regarding boundaries that most mental health professionals receive. In order for the AAT sessions to progress as smoothly as possible, it is important that the therapist and the volunteer address the issue of boundaries before the first AAT session. Boundary issues that should be covered include: client/volunteer boundaries, volunteer disclosure about themselves, volunteer disclosure to others regarding their experiences, sensitive subjects for the volunteer to avoid, when it is appropriate to converse with the client and/or therapist, what to do if they see the client outside the therapy environment and how the volunteer can be present in the therapeutic relationship between the therapist and the client. These issues cannot be fully addressed in volunteer orientation sessions because each therapist may have a different concept of appropriate boundaries. For this reason, it is vital that the therapist and the volunteer outline appropriate boundaries prior to any animal assisted therapy sessions. To necessitate clear communication and to ensure that the volunteer receives complete information regarding boundaries, the therapist can complete a form such as the 'Volunteer Boundary Information Form' found in the appendix.

Chapter 4: Starting Therapy

Examples Of FASD Behaviors That May Be
Treated Using AAT

AAT Activities That May Not Be Suitable For
FASD Clients

AAT Activities For Clients With
Developmental Disabilities

Who Is Not Suitable For AAT?

Setting Up An Evaluation System

Examples Of FASD Behavior That May Be Treated Using AAT

When working with clients with FASD, there are a few points to remember in order to have the most productive sessions as possible. It is important for therapists to have realistic expectations of their client's behavior and ability to change. Animal assisted therapy is not a 'magic bullet'; it is a valuable tool for therapists to use to help their clients. Therapists should not expect that animal assisted therapy will produce unrealistic improvements.

Clients with FASD perform best in a structured environment, and for this reason, animal assisted therapy should be provided in such an environment. This structure should include a few basic rules, set schedules, and use of the same therapy animal for all the sessions. Finally, clients with FASD may not have the cognitive capacity to understand abstract concepts and reasoning. In order to support a productive animal assisted therapy session, therapists should use only concrete and simple communication and teaching methods.

Here are some examples of animal assisted therapy goals and strategies for Bosco Homes' clients suffering from FASD:

Goal: Communication skills Strategy: Have client teach animal a new trick. Focus on client speaking clearly, not using too many words, selecting appropriate word for task, etc.
Goal: Self-care skills Strategy: Have a grooming session. Use this as an opportunity to teach appropriate self-care (how to comb hair, brush teeth, cut nails, etc.) while also teaching client how to care for an animal.
Goal: Mood elevation/ regulation Strategy: Allow client to have a positive experience with the animal engaging in whatever activity they enjoy (throwing a ball, going for a walk, cuddling the animal). Client will likely leave session in a positive mood, which may carry over to their next environment.

Goal: Appropriate emotional responses Strategy: Discuss and demonstrate how animal reacts to various situations (strangers, stressful situations, exciting situations, etc.), and role play appropriate client responses to similar situations.
Goal: Develop appropriate boundaries Strategy: Use an animal that is shy initially to demonstrate appropriate physical boundaries (the animal needs a 'bubble' of space to feel secure, can't touch it right away) and verbal boundaries (voice tone) etc.
Goal: Encouraging nurturing behavior. Strategy: Allow client to nurture the animal with appropriate rewards and affection.
Goal: Improve Ability to Trust. Strategies: • Talk to the animal. • Interact with and learn about the animal and its behaviors. • Receive affection from the animal.
Goal: Encourage bonding to a living being. Strategy: Give the client a photograph of themselves and the companion animal to help strengthen the bond between sessions. Strategy: Establish predictable routines for greeting and saying goodbye to the animal at each session.
Goal: Improve relationships with peers. Strategy: Use the relationships between the handler and the animal and between the therapist and the animal as a metaphor for human relationships. Work at transferring this experience to peers.
Goal: Increase amount of eye contact with people. Strategy: Work with the human-animal team to develop appropriate eye contact. Strategy: See how the animal uses eye contact Work at transferring that skill to other relationships.
Goal: Improve appropriateness of voice tone with people. Strategy: Work with the human-animal team to develop appropriate voice tone when training the animal. Notice how tone of voice affects the animal and its response to commands. Work at transferring this skill to other relationships.

Goal: Increase participation in group activities
Strategy: Use the animal as part of the group activity as incentive for participation. Have the animal 'invite' the individual to join the group.
Goal: Openly discuss feelings.
Strategy: Talk about traumatic events in the animal's life (e.g., being taken from its parents and siblings, going to live in a stranger's home, losing an owner due to illness, staying at a boarding kennel, getting in a fight with another animal), and ask the client to describe how the animal may have felt during these events.
Goal: Identify different emotions.
Strategy: When interacting with the animal in a variety of situations (e.g., excited to see them, eager to do a trick, bored by repetitive activity, ecstatic to see a toy, frustrated if they cannot have something they want, uncertain about a new activity, frightened by a loud noise, tired after a run, disappointed about not being allowed to play).
Goal: Acquire socially acceptable ways of expressing feelings.
Strategy: Observe and interact with the animal. Discuss the ways the animal expresses its feelings and what behaviors the client finds acceptable (e.g., prancing, wagging tail) or unacceptable (e.g., licking face, barking). Discuss self-control and how to regulate behaviors in human relationships and experiences.
Goal: Demonstrate patience and understanding.
Strategy: Teach the animal something new or try to get the animal to respond to obedience commands given by the client. Encourage patience, and teach the client how to get successful results. Have the client look for reasons why the animal may not be responding to their commands. The animal may be tired, the client may be doing a hand signal incorrectly, the animal may be uncomfortable doing the trick (i.e., Greyhounds find it difficult/painful to sit or lie down), the animal may be confused, etc.
Goal: Providing an opportunity to learn consequences of actions
Strategy: Show the client how to teach the animal a new trick. This learning process should include positive training strategies and how to help the animal succeed when learning.

Goal: Improve decision making and concentration. Strategy: Ask client what to do about a problematic behavior of the animal's (parallel to client's behavior when possible). Plan short-term goals and steps toward reaching goals. Apply process to client's situation. If client is a child, allow the child to decide what food treat to give the animal, which game to play, or when the animal needs to go out. Play "Simon says" and "Mother may I?" using the animal's name (e.g., Rufus says...) or the child's name (e.g., Jill says...Sit).
Goal: Increase assertiveness. Strategy: Practice role-playing assertive responses, with the animal as either an antagonist or a victim needing protection. Practice non-verbal assertion (tone of voice, eye contact, body posture).
Goal: Decrease anger outbursts and increase appropriate reactions to frustration. Strategy: When situations of frustration or nonsuccess arise while working with the human-animal team, use the opportunity to confront inappropriate or appropriate reactions. Reinforce appropriate responses to frustration and nonsuccess. Transfer the observations to relevant situations in the client's life.
Goal: Identify and reduce irrational thoughts which trigger or exacerbate anxiety. Strategy: Discuss possible origin and symptoms of the animal's irrational fears (e.g., thunder) and relate to client's fears when possible. Have client consider the origins of his own anxiety or phobia and identify the thoughts and sensations that trigger anxiety. Have client explain why the animal need not be afraid. Help client develop coping self-statements for his own situation.
Goal: Increase self-esteem/confidence Strategy: Have the handler say that they have been having trouble teaching the animal a trick. Teach the client how to train the animal to do the trick. Strategy: Talk with the client about what kind of care the therapy animal needs. Assign the client a task each session relating to caring for the animal's needs, such as brushing. Strategy: Have the client note how happy the therapy animal is to see them each session.

Goal: Learn About Appropriate Touch.
Strategies:
- Observe and discuss the animal's response to human touch.
- Learn gentle ways to handle the animal.
- Receive apparent acceptance from the animal.
- Give appropriate affection to the animal.
- Compare appropriate animal touch to appropriate human touch.
- Forecast "what would happen if...?"

AAT Activities That May Not Be Suitable For Clients With FASD

Due to the symptoms of FASD, not all animal assisted therapy activities may be appropriate for this client population. Clients with FASD often have cognitive difficulties that make it problematic for them to generalize behaviors.

For this reason, any strategies that require the client to generalize behavior learned while working with an animal to other situations may not be beneficial. These same cognitive difficulties may make it unreasonable to expect clients to understand complex strategies or metaphors, so strategies that use the animal as a metaphor, or require long explanations may not be suitable.

Consequences for negative behaviors and rewards for positive behaviors need to be immediate for most clients with FASD. Strategies that emphasize delayed rewards or focus on negative behavior after a period of time may have elapsed not produce the desired outcome. Over stimulation can be a problem for clients suffering from FASD.
Finally, a therapist should remember to keep animal assisted therapy strategies and activities at an optimum level of stimulation.

AAT Activities For Clients With Developmental Disabilities

There are a number of specific strategies for Animal Assisted Therapy sessions that therapists can use to help children with developmental disabilities achieve a variety of goals. This list represents a small sampling of options for helping children with disabilities. For additional goals and strategies, see the appendix of this manual.

Example AAT Goals and Strategies for Physiotherapists

Goal	Strategy
Improve upper mobility	Have the client hold out a hoop for the dog to jump through, brush the animal, hold out a target for the animal to touch, play fetch, pet the animal
Improve lower mobility	Have the client hold out their leg for the dog to jump over, play tug with the toy on their foot
Improve balance	Play fetch with the dog, and have the dog drop the ball near the client so they must bend and reach to pick up the ball Follow/race the dog through an agility course (bending/crawling through tunnels, stepping over small jumps) Go for walks with the dog High function: encourage the dog to pull on the leash, slow down, cross in front of client Low function: Use dog for balance assistance
Improve hand-eye coordination	Toss a large beach ball for the dog, encourage the dog to 'bop' it of the nose back to the client to catch Or play Frisbee with the dog and when the dog returns the Frisbee, toss it to the client

Improve core strength	Have the client play tug with the therapy dog (seated or standing)
Increase range of movement	Have the client stretch to pet the dog with hands (or feet), Have the client play fetch with the dog and stretch out to get the ball from the dog or the therapist Have the client stretch with the animal, or use the animal as a tool to help stretching (put leg up the back of a sitting dog)
Lower anxiety	Have the client pet the animal while undergoing treatment (such as stretching, Transcutaneous Electrical Nerve Stimulation/Electro Galvanic Stimulation, heat/cold, traction, etc.)
Improve Memory	Have client learn and recall information about the therapy dog, practice memory strategies
Improve fine motor skills	Practice dog-related tasks such as clipping a leash to a collar, brushing the animal, putting a jump bar into the jump cup, picking one small treat out of a bag to feed to the dog, etc.

Example Goals and Strategies for Occupational Therapists

Goal	Strategy
Reduced anxiety surrounding task	Have the client pet the animal while completing t[ ] task
Continue practicing task	Have the animal 'help' with task completion Ie. Have client practice putting socks on, have animal help take socks off
Increase functional mobility	Have client take the animal for a walk, introducing obstacles for function such as stairs, doors, etc.
Increase	Have the client practice skills on animal (ie.

personal care skills	Brushing teeth, getting animal dressed, brushing animal's hair)
Improve social skills	Practice new social skills with the animal
	Have the client take the animal for a walk and have client introduce the animal to those they meet (practice new social skills)
Improve attention skills	Have the client and dog 'compete' to see who can 'sit stay' the longest with a variety of distractions
	Use the therapy animal to redirect the client's attention back to the activity

Example Goals and Strategies for Recreational Therapists

Goal	Strategy
Show initiative/ motivation	Allow the client to choose what activities to do with dog
Participate in program-ming	Introduce the client to the animal, show tricks/petting and let the client know that the animal will be in programming if they would like to see more
Increase in activity	Let the client know that the therapy animal needs their help to get fit/reduce energy – it needs to go for a walk or have the client direct the dog through an agility course
Improve Mood	Play with the animal, see the animal's positive mood

Example Goals and Strategies for Social Workers

Goal	Strategy
Practice good parenting	Interact with the animal, practicing positive parenting skills (teaching new skills to the animal, correcting mistakes, rewarding good

skills	behavior)
Positive sibling interaction	Have siblings work together (practicing learned skills) to help the dog complete an agility course, or play fetch (taking turns)
Improve relationship	Have parent and child work together to have the dog complete a task Have the child learn how to instruct dog, then teach the parent
Improve attachment to parent/ reactive attachment disorder	Have the client interact/play with the dog (bond to the dog), then have parent and child play with dog (transfer the bond)

Example Goals and Strategies for Speech Language Pathologists

Problem	Goal	Strategy
Anxiety speaking in front of a group	Confidence speaking in groups	Start by speaking to the therapy animal, then have therapy animal accompany client when first speaking to group (to lower anxiety and divert attention from client)
Voice Disorders	Improve pitch, volume, quality, resonance or duration	Have the client use voice commands to get the dog to perform a task – the therapy dog only completes task when the client is speaking clearly
Articulation Disorders	Accurate reproduction of speech sounds	Have the client use problem sounds to instruct the dog (ie. Roll over, not oll over, saying the therapy dog's name before the trick command)

| Resistant to participate | Participate in activities | Have client follow instructions to work with the dog, such as placing toy then instructing the dog to retrieve it

Use the animal in activities (have client do skills to work with animal) |

Example Goals and Strategies for Psychologists

Problem	Goal	Strategy
PTSD	Improve functioning / reduce symptoms	Tell the client about the animals' past traumas (being taken away from mother, possible abuse, etc.) and ask client how the animal felt during those times. The client can project their own feelings onto the animal and feel more comfortable talking about it. Ask the client what the animal would like the animal handler to do to help when the client is having trouble with symptoms (another projection technique).
Anxiety	Reduce anxiety reactions	Have animal accompany client during anxiety producing event (such as fear of the dark or social interactions)
Failure to generalize skills	Generalize skills talked about in sessions	Provide experiential learning of new behaviors Problem solving – When the animal does not perform correctly (their reactions and/or situational cues for success)

| | | Conflict resolution – Two people work together to get therapy animal to perform task |
| | | Assertiveness – Enforcing personal space with therapy animal |

For additional psychology strategies, see appendix.

Example Goals and Strategies for Crisis Counselors

Problem	Goal	Strategy
Initial traumatic reaction	Help calm/comfort client	Encourage the client to hug/hold/pet therapy animal
Emotional difficulty in recounting event	Accurate, non-traumatic recollection of event for authorities	Have therapy animal present to reduce anxiety when filing the police report or testifying in court
Clients resistant to admit feelings related to trauma	Work through trauma related feelings	Have the client tell the animal their feelings or ask the client how the animal would feel in similar situation

For additional strategies, see appendix.

Example Goals and Strategies for School Counselors

Problem	Goal	Strategy
Students disliking/ avoiding counselor	Easy interactions between students and counselor	Have animal present, increases enjoyment of time

Stigma associated with 'seeing school counselor'	Reduce stigma	Present sessions as a 'treat' and as a chance to play with therapy animal
Poor social skills	Improve social skills/ standing	Have client play with therapy dog during recess/lunch as animal will act as attractant to other kids

For more strategies, see appendix.

Example Goals and Strategies for Psychiatrists

Problem	Goal	Strategy
Resistant client	Accurate assessments	Have the animal present during part of the assessment (introduce unpredictability/novel situations to assessment)
Anxious client	Reduce anxiety	Have animal present during assessment to reduce anxiety and paint more accurate picture of client functioning
Initial client discomfort with psychiatrist	Ease of initial interactions	Have therapy animal present (studies have shown that having an animal present can make a professional seem more trustworthy, worthy of disclosure and higher overall rated)

Example Goals and Strategies for Child and Youth Care Workers

Problem	Goal	Strategy
Client outbursts	Client can control their own outbursts	Draw attention to the animals reaction to the outburst (client doesn't want to upset animal)

Resistant to routine	Compliance with routines	Have the animal participate/initiate routine event (ie. Tucks clients in at night, wakes them up in the morning, 'helps' with homework)
Low fitness	Improved fitness	Have the clients take the dog for a walk, do agility, play soccer, etc.
Low trust in others	Increase trusting behaviors	Have the client make a bond with the therapy animal, point out no 'alternative agenda'
Low attendance in group programming	Increase attendance in group programming	Have therapy animal present/participating in group therapy
Poor self-image	Improved self-image	Identify strengths by asking what the therapy animal would say they like about the client, or how the client helps the therapy animal
Poor self-esteem	Improved self-esteem	Put the client 'in charge' of the therapy animal for the day
Poor social interactions	Improve social interactions	Have the clients work together to have the therapy animal complete a task (training, obstacle course, fetch)

Example Goals and Strategies for Nurses/Medical professionals

Problem	Goal	Strategy
Fear surrounding procedures	Reduction in fear	Show the client the procedure with the therapy animal (physical exams, taking ear temperature, using a

		stethoscope)
Anxiety surrounding procedure	Reduction in anxiety	Have therapy animal present during procedure
Restless during exams	Have client remain still	Use the therapy animal as a distraction

Example Goals and Strategies for Teachers/Teaching Aides

Problem	Goal	Strategy
Student is restless/disruptive	Reduce disruptions	Have the client sit at their desk with the therapy animal, pet as necessary
Classroom is loud	Reduce noise level	Allow the therapy dog to interact as long as noise level is low. If noise gets too loud then dog goes in kennel.
Difficulty reading	Enjoyment of reading	Have the client read to the therapy animal, read books about the therapy animal (Lassie books)
Poor attendance	Increased attendance	Have individual students participate in care of therapy animal (therapy animal needs to be cared for)
Lack of engagement in material	Increase enthusiasm	Engage in thematic learning about the therapy dog (biology of dogs, math surrounding feeding, social studies about dog breed origins, read/write stories about dogs, etc.)

Determining Who Is Not Suitable For AAT

Unfortunately, it is not possible for all clients to receive the benefits of animal assisted therapy. There are a number of instances where it is not advisable to use AAT including:

a) When the animal poses a risk to the client
   • Client is afraid of, or does not like animals (unless being treated for an animal-related phobia)
   • Client is allergic to animals
   • Client has open wounds or has low resistance to disease (immune compromised)

b) When the client or the environment poses a risk to the animal
   • Client is unable to handle the animal properly
   • Environment is unsafe or too stressful for the animal
   • Clients in a group rival for the animals attention (this type of rivalry is detrimental to the animal and to the therapeutic process)

c) When AAT would serve no beneficial purpose.

d) When client or their family (or other guardian) objects.

e) When the animal does not enjoy the interaction or when a client behaves in a manner that makes the animal uncomfortable. Sometime it is not possible to determine why an animal does not enjoy the interaction, but it is important to remove the animal if it is showing signs of discomfort.

f) When the person is from a cultural background that views animals differently. (e.g., farmers sometimes consider dogs and cats to be 'outside animals')

Setting Up An Evaluation System

The practice of animal assisted therapy is become more accepted as a modality of treatment for mental illness. Much of this change in public and professional opinion is due to the research that is being done in the field. As animal assisted therapy is still a novel treatment, it is essential that AAT programs set in place a procedure for evaluating their AAT program. These evaluations do not have to be lengthy or require excessive time to complete or analyze. Many residential treatment program or government funded programs require that records be kept, and these records can be used as a component of the evaluation. A benefit of using these evaluation measures is that the program can be compared to other similar programs, or to the national standardized scores.

Evidence-based practice is a continuing trend in mental health. Funding bodies want to know that their dollars are being spent on programs that are producing results. Some U.S. states now require that mental health programs operate on a 'Best Practice' or 'Evidence-Based Practice' model in order to receive any state funding. Furthermore, evidence-based practice signifies that a program is looking at its results and improving how its services are delivered. When a program evaluates its results, it is able to highlight its strengths, and attend to its weaknesses. This ultimately benefits the clients and ensures that they are receiving the best treatment possible. The source of evidence-based practice is good research, and the key to good research is good evaluation measures.

If specific outcomes are desired, it is possible to create high-quality evaluations, by following these steps:

1. Determine specifically what it is hoped will be achieved with the AAT program.

Is the program looking to increase self-esteem? Alleviate depression? Decrease anxiety? Increase empathetic behavior? Is the program hoping to reduce the number of times a client is restrained or secluded?

2. Find a valid measure of these variables. A local university may be able to help in the choice of a valid measure, such as:

The Beck Depression Inventory, the Youth Outcome Questionnaire, and the number of times a client is restrained a day.

3. Variables should be measured both before and after each AAT session as well as the entire AAT program. In addition, the facility's variables should be compared to those of similar facilities.

This procedure may sound difficult, but by using this process to create evaluations, a program ensures that their data is an accurate representation of their effectiveness. Using this process also allows the research to be presented at prestigious conferences and in
top-tier professional journals, and to contribute to furthering the field of animal assisted therapy.

If it is not possible to find a valid measure of the relevant variables (keeping in mind that there are over 300 psychological tests available), then it is possible to create a new measure. However, there are extensive drawbacks to this method. Self-created measures are not necessarily reliable or valid, and they have not been standardized. This means that they may not accurately measure what is intended to be measured, the evaluation tool may not be producing the same results in the same situations and it is not possible to chart improvement, compared to national standardized scores. Issues such as therapists needing to give extensive instructions and client/therapist misinterpretation of test items may also invalidate the data. It may also been assumed that a program created a tool to prove their program is effective, rather than using one that provides an unbiased report. Any data garnered from such measurement tools would likely not be publishable or presentable in top-tier professional conferences or journals. If a program needs to create their own measure, it is possible that a combination of standardized measures and created measures could be used. If a program is just looking for quick confirmation of their effectiveness, or is only investigating one small variable and is not concerned with limitations, then a created measure may be the best choice.

It is also possible to measure the success of an AAT program through simple recording of data. Therapists can measure attendance, participation (how many times a client performed the task) or length of sessions and compare AAT sessions to non-AAT sessions. In this way, therapists can show outcomes such as: a 20% increase in attendance when AAT was occurring, the doubling of the number of times a client made the 'sp' sound, or sessions lasting an average of 20 minutes longer when AAT was occurring.

Chapter 5: Issues During Therapy

What The Clients Say About AAT

Therapists' Experiences With AAT

- Lauren

- Anna

- Mathews

- Sonia

What The Clients Say About Animal Assisted Therapy

The following provide some anecdotal quotes of the benefits from the AAT sessions seen through the eyes of the clients at Bosco Homes. The clients were asked if they liked having the animals with them in their therapy sessions. These are some of their replies.

"Yes, because it helps."

"Yes, because they are not as mean as humans and they help me."

"Because they understand"

"The animal helps me talk to the therapist."

"...it makes me happy when they're around and makes me feel better about myself, and also makes me feel confident about my self."

"They make me feel a lot safer."

"Duke is a cool dog. He is always happy to see me... He makes me feel happy when he is there. Duke is the most awesome dog I have met."

"[The AAT session] helps me stay calm and happy"

"The animal helps me talk to staff and feel good about something. I feel better after."

"The dog was cuddling with me and that made me happy. It's easier to smile with the dog."

"AAT makes me happy when I am around and makes me feel better about myself, and also makes me feel confident about myself."

"...helps calm me down when I am angry - helps me to do my work."

"The animal helps me talk about my past and helps me be more happier about myself and safe."

"The dog is a good friend."

Therapists' Experiences With Animal Assisted Therapy

During the three-year study period at The Chimo Project, a number of our therapists[13] found that animal assisted therapy significantly helped a number of their clients suffering from Fetal Alcohol Spectrum Disorder (FASD). These are their stories.

Lauren – Occupational Therapist at Bosco Homes Intensive Treatment Center

- There was one fifteen-year-old boy that had real trouble communicating. It's not like he couldn't; he just didn't communicate his problems really well. He felt very disconnected from his family. They were not making the necessary steps in order to get him home, and I think he was getting the message that they didn't really want him anymore. He was really feeling rejection from his family. He was very lonely.

  I didn't really have a plan for him using the dog, but the dog seemed to sense in the boy that he needed comfort. The boy would just sit down on the floor of the office, and the dog would walk over and press her forehead on his forehead. They would just sit there like that for twenty minutes at a time. He was responsive to questions when the dog was doing this, but sometimes we were just silent and let the dog do her own therapy. The boy always reported feeling better after the sessions with the dog. He seemed to really need that unconditional love and acceptance.

---

[13] The therapists' middle names are used to protect the privacy of the clients.

The staff can't provide unconditional acceptance. When the boy got into trouble and would be disciplined, the boy saw that as judgmental and not caring: more rejection, just like his family. The dog sensed in this boy the need for unconditional love, and was the only one who could provide it.

- One twelve-year-old girl was depressed. Most normal therapy sessions were spent with her sitting with her legs crossed, her arms crossed, sulking. She was snarky and unhappy. A very difficult kid to work with. I knew that she loved animals, so I asked if she wanted to be part of the animal assisted therapy program. She did, and when she was with the dog, she was a totally different girl. She was smiling, happy, laughing, and making jokes. They spent a lot of time on the floor playing with each other. When she was around the dog, her body language changed. She was sitting up, making eye contact. Instant mood improvement.

- A fifteen-year-old boy came to therapy that really didn't have a family. His language was very hard to understand. He mumbled, spoke quickly, and couldn't regulate his tone, which was always flat. He didn't understand the need for enunciation and tone of voice in communication. I used the dog to work on his communication as a social skill. The boy taught the dog some new tricks, working on using appropriate tone and language to encourage the dog to respond. He used fewer words, spoke slowly, and did not mumble. There was great improvement in his speech skills and how to use words and appropriate tone. Once he was able to get the dog to complete the task, I had him demonstrate the tricks to the other kids in his class. This boy was often ostracized by his classmates. He had low self-esteem, no friends, and wasn't really good at anything. This demonstration proved to the boy that he was important.

He had a special relationship with the dog, and the kids in his class were impressed by that. It really helped this boy's self-esteem and social skills, as well as his communication skills.

- There was another boy who was fourteen. He had very poor boundaries. He was always getting into trouble hugging people without asking. He definitely had a need for physical contact, but as therapists in this situation we cannot ethically fulfill that need. I used the dog to teach this boy boundaries. I showed him that when the dog is not comfortable, when its boundaries are being violated, it will back off. Once the boy was comfortable learning about the dog's boundaries, I let him play with the dog. They rolled around on the floor together, and the dog covered him with kisses. He really liked those dog kisses. It just provided a time for appropriate, positive physical contact. It allowed this boy to meet his need for physical contact in an appropriate way.

- One fourteen-year-old boy literally would not talk in therapy. Not a word. He had been involved with gangs and was very unhappy to be away from his family. Another therapist was having no success with this boy, so it was suggested that he might benefit from animal assisted therapy. I took the dog to the residential house he was in. The boy met the dog, sat on the floor, and started asking me questions about the dog. He was quite happy to talk about the dog in our sessions. When the dog was there, his face went from stony to soft. He was getting more comfortable and becoming more ready to talk. The dog created a safe place for him to talk. I was just trying to get him into a better space, because if you can get them happy in the moment, their behavior will be good in the moment.

- Due to the boy's improving family situation, he was discharged after a few AAT sessions, but I think if they had been able to continue that the dog would have really helped the boy open up.

Anna – Therapist at Bosco Homes Intensive Treatment Center

- One twelve-year-old boy came to me presenting with symptoms of depression and anxiety and had poor peer relationships. He was feeling displaced and abandoned. This kid was also bullied by the kids at school. This boy had social phobia and the therapy cat became a safe way to initiate conversation. The cat was a safe companion because when the cat was in the cat shelter, he was bullied by the other cats too. So the cat understood, and the boy liked the cat very much. The cat also provided unconditional positive regard. The boy remarked that he felt safe with the cat because he won't say, "Shut up you fatso." Like the kids at school. So in the therapy sessions, while the boy talked, he petted the cat, snuggled with him, and focused on the cat instead of on the therapist. He could keep talking about difficult issues when he was petting the cat.

- A fifteen-year-old girl came to me with issues of displacement, abandonment, anxiety, and depression. She also had difficulty processing past sexual abuse. She was able to assert herself in a positive way when the cat entered her personal space and was kneading her legs. I asked her if she was comfortable with the cat, and she said "No". I asked her if she was going to do anything about her discomfort. She sat up and said, "Yes. I am going to move him off my lap." It provided a non-threatening situation where she could exercise her boundaries in a positive manner.

- When confronting her fear issues, the girl was able to produce coping thoughts for the cat and herself. She told the cat, that when he was afraid of something he should tell himself, "Don't worry. You'll be okay. You've been brave before, and you can be brave again."

- Another fourteen-year-old girl was in therapy because she had trouble recognizing personal safety issues and was misusing substances. We talked about how the cat had been a street cat for a while before he got picked up by the cat shelter. She had been a street kid, and that is where most of her issues came from. We talked about what kinds of issues the cat had to deal with on the street to keep himself safe. We talked about getting food, shelter, and how to deal with being abandoned. She came to the conclusion that the group home was like the cat shelter the therapy cat had been in.

- We also talked about her substance misuse problems. Rather than address it directly, we talked about how the cat had a problem with scratching the carpet. We talked about how scratching the scratching post is okay, but not the entire carpet. She asked how the cat had solved his problems, and we talked about how the cat needed help from others to deal with his habit. The cat now wears claw-caps, and I am helping him get through. I focused on how sometimes it's okay to need help from others to get over your bad habit.

- A sixteen-year-old girl came to therapy who was feeling displaced and abandoned. She said that she was not fitting in with her family anymore. She was worried about what happens when you don't fit in with your family. I told her that the cat was abandoned by his family because he was not fitting in. She picked up the cat and hugged him, letting him into her world. She began talking about things she had never talked about before. She was calmed by holding the cat when she was recounting stories of her past abuse. She just kept hugging him and talking.

Mathews – Therapist at Bosco Homes

- I worked with a fourteen-year-old female client who had issues with trust and boundary issues. I had been working with her for six months in individual therapy before beginning animal assisted therapy with her. She had trouble with trust, and if she doesn't trust, she doesn't open up. Any attempts to confront her on uncomfortable issue would result in her shutting down, so I thought animal assisted therapy might be beneficial. In the first few sessions of AAT, she opened up and revealed instances of parental abuse that she had not felt comfortable talking about in the six months of traditional therapy. She recalled memories of her own pet as a source of love and support. She really connected with the dog. She felt that the dog created a trusting atmosphere and was able to open up.

- There was one ten-year-old male who had suffered from severe neglect. He now had impulsivity issues, lack of empathy, and poor boundaries. He had been having AAT sessions for a while when one of the sessions had to be cancelled due to the dog's illness. This boy showed an incredible level of empathy. Without any prompting, he composed a get-well card for the dog and (again, without any cues) went up to his classroom and had all his classmates sign the card. This was well above and beyond the level the kid had been functioning at before he met the dog.

- Another ten-year-old boy had ADHD and poor boundaries. He was very hyperactive towards the dog in the sessions. He took a toy and wiggled it at the dog's face. The dog withdrew to the other side of the room. When the boy asked why the dog left, I took that as an opportunity to teach him in the moment about the importance of boundaries. I pointed out the error, that the dog wasn't comfortable; his boundaries were violated, so he withdrew. It was important for the boy to understand that there are appropriate ways of conducting yourself when dealing with other living creatures. So we revisited the situation with the boy's new knowledge of boundaries. He called the dog over and the dog responded. The boy made note of the dog's boundaries, and when they were observed, the dog stayed with the boy.

- One fourteen-year-old female had real difficulty expressing her needs. She also has family issues of abandonment. She displayed a lot of extreme behaviors like self-harm, and in sessions she was evasive. She was silly, used silence, distractions and withdrawal to avoid discussion and confrontation. She was difficult to communicate with. When introduced to animal assisted therapy, she initiated a lot of appropriate physical interaction. She connected with the animal on a deep level. Her verbal communication improved greatly. Her deep connection with the dog enabled her to communicate with me.

Sonia – Therapist at Bosco Homes Intensive Treatment Center

For deeply wounded individuals, having an animal there provides them with an opportunity to open themselves up and open up that very wounded part without feeling at all threatened because the animal is totally accepting. The therapy dog is so big and laid back; they feel that there is nothing they could do to upset him. They feel totally safe on a very basic human level. It is different than two humans interacting.

The animal also tends to kinesthetically provide the nervous system with a certain amount of soothing. The therapy animal tends to almost release some of the tension in the client's nervous system. I noticed this with all clients to varying degrees. With an animal, there is no need for defenses. Two honest beings, facing each other, eye to eye. No need for pretension, or defenses. It is valuable for our clients to occasionally experience no need for masks. Even if it's only momentary, it gives them a new experience. Then as a therapist I can build on that.

- There was one fourteen-year-old boy that was withdrawn and hostile. He felt very threatened by the world. It took a number of weeks to develop trust before I introduced animal assisted therapy. As soon as AAT was introduced, I noticed that some of his defensiveness began to subside. In conjunction with one-on-one therapy and AAT, his sense of humor began to emerge; suggesting a lightening of his intensity and his sadness. There was a part that had been walled away entirely. With the weekly AAT, those walls became thinner and thinner. As a result he felt less and less threatened by the outside world and became more wiling to comply with site regulations. This didn't happen overnight, but over time. Now he's been one of the best-behaved clients in the house. I attribute part of that to the connection with the dog. He is the only one I see in that house with AAT.

- I had one young boy who resisted AAT because he could feel himself softening. The dog cut through defenses, and he started acting more his age. It was a new experience, new feeling. He withdrew. Now I only see him in one-on-one therapy. It was interesting to watch how he knew that something was changing, and it was making him more vulnerable.

The dog helps the clients to access parts of themselves that have been closed off. They become soft emotionally with the soft animal. These kids have formed a protective shell due to trauma. The animal assisted therapy has a way of permeating the shell in an effective way, then that opens the door for the therapist to engage. Animal assisted therapy has the potential to accelerate the speed of recovery. Coupled with client centered therapy and the right individual, it really can accelerate the healing process.

Chapter 6: Lessons Learned

Chimo Project Lessons Learned

Lessons Learned From Our Programs

Chimo Project Lessons Learned

Volunteer recruitment and retention

One of the major challenges our animal assisted therapy program faces on a regular basis is the recruitment and retention of volunteers. Our program manager regularly spends numerous hours per week recruiting, training, and retaining volunteers. Finding new volunteers requires advertising and attendance at Pet Expo's and community dog events. Training volunteers takes at least four hours per volunteer, and often the volunteers need encouragement in getting through the AAT program's screening tests and the orientation procedures at a facility. Without this encouragement they can become discouraged and leave the program before they even begin volunteering. It is also important to retain volunteers by having recognition days, sending the dogs cookies on their birthdays, tracking volunteer progress, presenting them with progress certificates, and checking in with the volunteers personally at least once a month.

The originators of this program did not foresee the large amount of time and resources needed for this part of the program. The lesson learned was that an animal assisted therapy program must plan to allocate a large portion of their resources to recruiting, training, and retaining volunteers.

Animal Name Tags and Therapy Dog Vests

It is important that when an animal is visiting or working at a facility that they have proper identification as a therapy animal. At the beginning of the program the volunteer animals were provided with quick-release bandanas for identification. A number of volunteers were not happy with the bandanas. They were cumbersome and the handlers felt that they interfered with the clients petting the dogs. The bandanas were then replaced with facility name tags, complete with the animals' picture. These tags also had the animal's name and identification as a therapy animal. The handlers loved the idea – it seemed novel that their animal would get its own name tag. The staff and clients also benefited from the change, as it provided a topic of conversation. The name tags also lend credibility to the animal and the AAT program through the tag's perceived authority.

The use of therapy dog vests is another way to show authority of the certified animals and to increase volunteer/staff buy-in into the AAT program.

Dog House

As one of the first tasks at one of the facilities, a dog house/run was created for the dogs to use while they are on site at the facility. The intention was for this to be a place where the dogs could relax between animal assisted therapy sessions, or where the handlers could take their dogs if an unexpected situation arose where the handler could not be with the dog. However, after the dog run was created, it was noticed that it was not being used by any of the handlers. In fact, the staff had allocated a dog-friendly manager's office where the dogs would be taken if they needed to be kenneled. When asked why they did not use the specially created kennel, the staff replied that they would not feel their dog was safe being outside in the kennel. Despite the fact the kennel was locked, made of chain link, entirely enclosed, and in a highly visible location, the staff members were concerned that their animal might be harmed by the children in treatment. They stated that the clients often go 'AWOL' and that not all the clients at this facility could be trusted around animals. Due to this concern they developed their contingency plan of kenneling their dogs in a manager's office. They chose this particular office because the manager was animal-friendly, and was in her office for most of the day, so the dog would never be left unattended.

In the future, it would be beneficial for animal assisted therapy programs to look at both sides of an issue concerning the animal's safety. The creation of a kennel was to ensure that the animals were as comfortable as possible during their visits; however, programs also need to include concerns about the animal's safety and the handler's need to ensure the animals safety (including 'what if's?' with worst case scenarios) before proceeding.

Creating a self-sustaining program

Many programs need extensive support to get an animal assisted therapy program running at their facility. However, it is crucial that the AAT programs do not require this high level of support forever. No program can sustain itself through the continuous efforts of one person. Programs need to become diverse and self-sufficient in order to survive. Based on the success of the 'Eden Alternative' self-sufficient programs and the observations from our AAT programs, the following steps have been devised to ensure that the animal assisted therapy program is sustainable.

Steps to creating a self-sufficient animal assisted therapy program

1. Determine the AAT Program Manager for the facility.

2. Create a core committee/group for the facility, which meets once a month to discuss the AAT program. This committee includes:
   a. A therapist from each specialty at the facility (psychologist, child and youth care worker, mental health nurse, recreational therapist, etc.)
   b. A representative from administration
   c. A representative from infrastructure
   d. An expert on the client base
   e. A volunteer handler (if used in program)
   f. An animal expert (trainer, veterinarian, etc.)
   g. A Chimo Project representative
   h. AAT Program Manager

The core committee decides on the specific mission, vision, goals, scope, and objectives for the AAT program at the facility, and identifies primary and secondary stakeholders.

3. Introduce the concept of AAT at the regular facility managers' meeting.

4. Hold an open forum for interested people to come and hear about the new AAT program:
   a. Have a Question & Answer (Q&A) brochure ready for the meeting and have all core committee members carry these with them.
   b. Post Q&A sheets with name of person to contact for more information. Include both phone and email contacts.

5. Post the mission, vision, goals, etc., in a visible place in the facility.

6. Begin training the therapists.

7. Begin acquiring/training/testing the animals.

8. Develop subcommittees:
   a. Pet Committee – makes decisions about animals.
   b. Solutions Committee – handles complaints in an unbiased manner.
   c. Education Committee – handles new recruits and decides on new material to be included in education; also decides what training is needed for the facility and how that training will be done.
   d. Evaluations Committee – gathers questionnaires, analyses them, sends out data.
   e. The 'Welcome Waggin' Committee – gets the word out about AAT to other staff members, families, clients, other similar facilities, and the community

at large (primary and secondary stakeholders). During the initial implementation phase, this committee keeps everyone posted about the progress of the program.

9. Create a pilot program with one highly motivated therapist and one animal. This will allow a program to work out all the kinks before more widely adopting the AAT program.

10. Put up notices on the wall of area/unit that the AAT program will be beginning in a specified area of the facility and also the name of person to contact for more information.

11. If using volunteer handlers, have an orientation meeting with the volunteer, the animal, all staff members they will be working with, and potential clients. Determine exact client treatment plans with the therapist before the volunteer begins regular visits.

12. Before the first AAT session hold one last open forum for people to meet and express their ideas about the program.

13. Begin scheduled therapy work.

14. Continue training therapists and animals.

15. If the pilot program is performing well, then begin therapy with other therapists and animals (using steps 10-12 for every new area/therapist involved).

16. Continue to discuss AAT at every manager's meeting.

17. Have core committee meet once a month; other committees on an as-needed basis (at least once every 2-3 months).

Lessons Learned From Our Programs

In order to best understand the strengths and areas of improvement for ours and future animal assisted therapy programs, questionnaires were created and distributed to everyone involved in our animal assisted therapy programs.
The responses have been divided into three categories. General stakeholders included facility program coordinators and volunteer coordinators. The volunteer animal handlers are another category and the therapists included psychologists and occupational therapists.

Lessons Learned from General Stakeholders
There are many strengths in the way animal assisted therapy is being implemented at a number of facilities. General stakeholders believed that this program of AAT offered good training for the therapists and volunteers involved. They also responded that the staff was very personable and they received good ongoing support. Finally they also responded that they could see the benefits of animal assisted therapy in the clients.

Strengths:
- Good training
- Knowledgeable, personable, helpful staff
- Good support with the program coordinators
- Seeing the benefits to the clients

There is always room for improvement in any program. These stakeholders believed that this program needed to work harder to retain volunteers, including streamlining the process to get volunteers trained and oriented and making sure that the volunteer's expectations of animal assisted therapy sessions are accurate. While this program had strong support for the coordinators, there was a feeling that the support for the house managers was lacking. These stakeholders were also unsure about the evaluations process for the animal assisted therapy program.

Lessons Learned:
- Have as simple a process as possible to screen, train and orient volunteers
- Make sure that volunteers understand what AAT will be like at the facility
- Ensure that all stakeholders receive support, including management at all levels
- It is not essential for all stakeholders to be involved in all the AAT processes. However these stakeholders do benefit from knowing the details of each step in the process

<u>Lessons Learned from Volunteers</u>

The volunteers were happy with a number of aspects of the animal assisted therapy program. Volunteers felt that they were appreciated for their work. They believed they have received enough training to perform their tasks. The volunteers valued that most of the therapists were well trained in animal assisted therapy and understood how to use their animal. The therapist's ongoing support was also beneficial. The volunteers also felt that the clients in the AAT program were well chosen, and that the clients in the program were benefiting from the AAT program. Staff persistence during the training process and good animal testing procedures were also highlighted by the volunteers.

Strengths:
- The volunteers felt that their work was appreciated
- A good level of volunteer training for AAT
- Knowledgeable therapists that make the most of their animal
- The clients were well chosen for the AAT program
- They could see the clients benefiting from the AAT program

- Program persistence during the screening, training and orientation procedures
- Good animal testing/screening procedures

The volunteers also raised some ideas on how the animal assisted therapy program could be enhanced. The volunteers felt that follow-ups and program support could be improved. Enhancements included documenting volunteer time, checking up on them at least once and month, therapists providing session feedback and providing the volunteers with some client feedback. The volunteers also felt that some areas of implementation and evaluation were lacking. They noted that not all therapists knew how to use the animal in the session properly. They also highlighted the need for a volunteer networking group and encouraged more advertising for the program.

Lessons Learned:
- Document volunteer time
- Check on each volunteer personally at least once a month
- Have the therapists provide them with session feedback regularly
- Provide volunteers with clients feedback (names removed)
- Streamline implementation
- Ensure that all therapists are using AAT properly
- Create a volunteer networking group
- Advertise the program as much as possible

Lessons Learned from Therapists
The therapists noted a number of assets in the animal assisted therapy program. Comprehensive training, good written materials and strong support were all emphasized. The therapists appreciated being a part of developing the AAT program and the evaluations that are used. Therapists enjoyed the opportunity to participate in a program that was researched with continued outcome measures. They liked that

animal assisted therapy was part of a formalized system of treatment, not just 'bringing a pet to work'. The therapists valued the accommodating, dedicated volunteers. The enthusiasm the clients showed anticipating and during AAT sessions was also encouraging. The therapists also valued being able to advocate the benefits of animal assisted therapy through events such as press conferences.

Strengths:
- Comprehensive training in AAT
- Good written materials
- Strong support from the project
- Including the therapists in the implementation and evaluation process
- The ability to be part of a program conducting research
- A formalized program of AAT
- The dedicated volunteer handlers
- Client enthusiasm for the program
- Opportunities to advocate AAT

The therapists also underscored areas that could be improved in the animal
assisted therapy program. There were instances where therapists had been trained in AAT, but a suitable animal match was difficult to find due to scheduling. This emphasizes a need for more volunteers with daytime availability. The therapists believed that there was a need to standardize the evaluation measures used. They also highlighted the need to be less reliant on subjective measures for evaluations such as, "I feel that the AAT work with the client helps him/her to perform better overall socially." The length of the evaluations was also a concern to the therapists. A more formalized therapists' networking group was suggested. The therapists suggested that they would like to have a wide variety of animals and species to work with.

Finally, the therapists mentioned that more AAT therapy goals and strategies could be developed.

Lessons Learned:
- **Recruit and train more volunteers**
- **Find volunteers with daytime availability**
- **Standardize evaluation measures**
- **Rely less on subjective measures**
- **Ensure the evaluations are as short as possible**
- **Have a wide variety of animals and species for AAT sessions**
- **Create a formal therapists network**
- **Create additional AAT goals and strategies**

Conclusions

The primary conclusion of this three-year demonstration project is that **the use of Animal Assisted Therapy (AAT) in the treatment of youth suffering from Fetal Alcohol Spectrum Disorder (FASD) is beneficial and has assisted those clients who have participated in the program. This project has produced sufficient positive results to merit continuation and expansion of the concept.** In addition to the survey results every therapist involved in this project has indicated that animal assisted therapy has been beneficial to each of their clients. In past and current other programs only one therapist believed one of her clients did not receive benefit from AAT.

In addition to this general statement, a number of potentially helpful conclusions have been reached:

a) The results are fully consistent with the original Chimo research project and the Capital Health demonstration project now underway. It is therefore reasonable to conclude that this assist to therapy enhances the effect of therapy on those suffering from a variety of mental health challenges/conditions.

b) In order for an AAT program to be successful, it must have substantial lead time. This time is required for staff at all levels of a facility (janitorial to therapy) to develop comfort with the AAT approach. Substantial time for the orientation of therapists and the recruitment of volunteers is also required. Experiences to date indicate that one year is the average lead time required.

c) It is not adequate to develop a program, orient staff, train volunteers and animals, and expect the program to then continue on its own. Constant turnover of staff and volunteers requires an ongoing training and orientation dimension.

d) Volunteers are expected to travel and give up their time in addition to training their animal and getting them through the required obedience and temperament tests. Some of the turnover of volunteers is a result of the financial contribution volunteers must make. A small honorarium (e.g. $10 per visit) could help to stabilize the volunteer pool, which has not yet been adequate to provide appropriate animals to all who would wish to avail themselves of this therapy adjunct.

e) Due to the strict acceptance requirements implemented by the Chimo Project, no negative incident has ever taken place while using AAT. Funders could assist in the introduction of AAT into youth treatment programs by insisting that all insurance for such centers include the use of animal assisted therapy in its policy. The inclusion of AAT in a policy should not require additional costs. Concern and negotiation over insurance has held up AAT program development for long periods of time, for example, at the Yellow Head Youth Center.

f) An ongoing training and orientation center would be beneficial for youth treatment programs wishing to begin an AAT program as well as those that are currently in operation. This may enable more treatment centers to implement AAT programs, which would improve access to AAT in Alberta and enhance the evolution of this form of therapy.

Helping clients suffering from FASD is often a difficult undertaking. Given the array of symptoms and the differing severities of the disorder, no two people suffering from FASD can be treated in the same way. Animal assisted therapy offers an innovative solution to care for these clients. The therapy animals are a friend, a playmate, and a sympathetic ear. They provide the clients with unconditional love, a reason to actively participate in therapy sessions, and an opportunity to learn new skills in a supportive environment.

Therapists are using animal assisted therapy as a tool for addressing FASD related symptoms such as poor communication skills, aversion to communication, boundary issues, feelings of abandonment and rejection, and an inability to think in an abstract or theoretical manner.

In the programs at Bosco Homes, it was found that there are a number of benefits to matching FASD clients with therapy animals. Animal assisted therapy was found to increase communication, self-esteem, positive self-image, and confidence while decreasing anxiety and depression. Clients felt more comfortable with their therapists, more able to do their assigned tasks, and more able to talk about their feelings. They looked forward to therapy sessions. The therapists involved felt that the clients found comfort in the animal, settled faster, wanted to come to therapy, and were willing to stay longer. The youth were more able to concentrate and their mood was improved during their sessions.

This manual provides practitioners with a practical action plan for implementing an animal assisted therapy program. There are many steps involved with creating, implementing and evaluating such a program. There are issues to be addressed in order to create a successful AAT program such as site assessment, policies and procedures, insurance, criteria for which animals to use, animal testing and screening, therapist training, and client selection. While it is important that these issues be addressed, it is also essential that each program and practitioner adapt the information found in this manual to best fit their particular program. In the programs whose results contributed to this manual, there were a number of lessons learned that will help improve animal assisted therapy programs in the future.

The Chimo Project program is the first of its kind to use animal assisted therapy to help residential youth clients suffering from FASD. It is hoped that the information in this manual will assist other programs across the nation and around the globe use therapy animals to help clients who suffer from the effects of Fetal Alcohol Spectrum Disorder.

Appendices

Additional Information
Global policies and procedures
AAT general strategies

Therapist and program forms
Checklist for selecting appropriate clients
A therapist's checklist for AAT sessions
AAT intervention planning worksheet
AAT session tracking sheet
Client referral form
Incident report
Waiver release and indemnity
Professional/Client treatment information release
    consent
Volunteer release form
Volunteer confidentiality agreement
Therapist questionnaire
Client questionnaire
Volunteer boundary information form

Animal information and forms
Staff animal survey
Dog obedience testing form
Dog obedience testing score sheet
Cat/small animal obedience testing form
Cat/small animal testing score sheet
Canine good neighbor test
Health screening form
Temperament testing form

(Sample) Global Policies and Procedures

Scope	This policy applies to all treatment areas.
Purpose	This policy establishes guidelines by which this facility arranges AAT for appropriate inpatients/outpatients.
Audience	This information in this document is intended for all staff members and the volunteer AAT animal handlers recruited for the program.
Policy	The AAT program will serve as part of the comprehensive care program provided by therapeutic staff to patients.
Rationale for AAT	AAT is a goal-directed therapeutic intervention that focuses on helping clients discover parts of themselves through interacting with a skilled animal and a professional mental health practitioner who is skilled in human-animal interactions. AAT is an opportunity for patients to let down their guard, increase their motivation, develop trust, and feel good about themselves. Mental health patients often have issues such as poor attachment/bonding, low self-esteem, difficulty with feelings of empathy, poor boundaries with others, depression, difficulty maintaining attention, anxiety, sexual/physical/emotional abuse, traumas, separation, and loss issues. This program provides a non-threatening context for patients to discover and explore these capacities. Applying these capacities towards self and others is one of the goals of this program.
General Guidelines	• Animals participating in AAT must be screened for appropriateness and temperament, and at all times be accompanied by their handler. • If any patient is bitten, scratched, or has any adverse reaction to animals, staff will initiate any necessary emergency procedures, notify the nurse and physician, and the AAT handler will remove the animal immediately and will not bring the animal to visit again. An Incident Report will be completed.
AAT	• Animals will work with patients who have no

Patient Criteria	contraindications for AAT:
	o allergies (limit or avoid exposure)
	o immune-suppressed
	o fear or dislike of animals
	o aggression towards animals.
AAT Animal Criteria	• All AAT animals must meet the following guidelines:
	o Be under a veterinarian's care
	o Be free of parasites, ticks, fleas
	o Have current vaccinations, as recommended by the veterinarian
	o Be free of lesions or dramatic hair loss
	o Be bathed or groomed within the 24 hours prior to the visit
	o Have nails trimmed and sharp edges filed
	o Have appropriate skills and aptitude, as determined by The Chimo Project screening guidelines: Canadian Canine Good Citizen certification and The Chimo Project Aptitude exam.
	• Handlers will check animals for cleanliness, fleas, general health, and temperament immediately prior to each visit.
	• Handlers will allow the animals to exercise and eliminate before AAT and provide ample water and rest before and during AAT.
	• Animals must be on a leash, carried, or in a pet carrier upon entry and exit from the facility.
	• Animals are to be on-leash or within reach of the handler at all times.
	• Animals will be accompanied by the handler at all times.
Volunteer AAT Handler Criteria	• People who wish to volunteer for the AAT program must be approved by the Alberta Hospital Volunteer Coordinator.
	• Handlers must wear name tags while in the facility.
	• Handlers will work under the direction of the staff members in the program they are working with.
	• Handlers will be free of contagious diseases and

avoid visiting if they have been exposed to a contagious disease.

- Handlers with infectious diseases, viruses, fever, or who have knowingly been exposed to contagious diseases are not to visit without prior approval of the facility.
- Handlers will supervise, discipline, and control animals by leash, command, and/or time-out at all times during AAT. Handlers will control inappropriate animal behavior such as licking, jumping, barking, growling, and biting.
- Animals are to be on-leash or within reach of the handler at all times.
- Animals will be accompanied by AAT handler at all times.

Sanitation and Infection Control	<ul><li>It is recommended that anyone who touches the animal wash their hands immediately after. Handlers and therapists should do the same, and it is recommended that they also wash their hands before touching the animal.</li><li>Handlers and animals must enter and exit facility through the designated main entrance and take a direct route to the respective patient care area.</li><li>The following are off-limits areas at all times with an animal:<ul><li>Kitchen areas</li><li>Medication rooms</li><li>Nursing Stations (i.e., desk area)</li><li>Food preparation and storage areas</li><li>Eating areas (dining or patient rooms during meals) – Exceptions: Seeing-eye Dogs and Service Dogs</li><li>Clean or sterile supply storage rooms</li><li>Tub rooms.</li></ul></li><li>Appropriate areas where AAT will occur will be designated and limited. Rooms that are not carpeted should be selected for easy clean-up. It is recommended that the room where AAT occurs be swept and damp-mopped following AAT to reduce</li></ul>

allergens.

- If an animal is allowed on furniture (beds, chairs), a clean sheet should be laid on the furniture first. After the animal leaves, the sheet should be rolled up and placed into the laundry and the person removing the sheet washes their hands.
- An appropriate area (relatively low traffic) will be designated for the animal to exercise and eliminate. It is recommended that plastic bags be readily available within this area to pick up after the animals and that a garbage nearby be designated for waste disposal.
- Handlers will deal with indoor bodily accidents by:
  o Placing solid material in a plastic bag
  o Spraying the area with disinfectant
  o Wiping the area with a clean paper-towel
  o Disposing of the paper towel in the plastic bag
  o Placing secured plastic bag in designated area or container
  o Washing hands immediately
  o Documenting the accident.
- When an accident occurs on a patient or on patient's belongings,
  o the handler will clean up the animal waste
  o staff or housekeeping (Environmental Services) will be notified immediately to disinfect the area
  o The accident will be documented in an Incident Report.

Facility Requirements	• AAT is to occur only in pre-approved areas. Records of animal visits must be kept to ensure allergic patients are not placed in the same room within 24 hours of the visit.
	• The responsibilities of staff are to:
	  o Consider the potential allergic reaction and convenience of all patients and staff, and assess for allergies and phobias prior to visits from any animal
	  o Screen patients to ensure they are appropriate

for AAT activities
o Notify handlers of patients who should not work with animals due to contraindications: patients with unpredictable or aggressive behavior should be identified and monitored
o Minimize the potential for the animals to come into contact with medications and hazardous materials – on tabletops, floors, in clients' pockets, etc. A careful visual check of the AAT room assists in ensuring the safety of the animal.
o Schedule AAT sessions with the handlers
o Make patients, families, and team members aware of AAT opportunities
o Maintain open communication with The Chimo Project as the AAT program facilitators
o Notify housekeeping for clean-up, if necessary.

Table 1: Example goals and strategies to develop
rapport and foster relationships.

TREATMENT GOALS	AAT STRATEGY
Deepen trust with therapist (transference).	Permit the client to hold or pet the companion animal while interacting with the therapist or the therapy group.
Develop rapport with therapist.	The animal may be a common interest between the therapist and client and, thus, can create a bond and foster discussion.
Increase social interaction skills.	• Encourage the client to talk to the animal rather than the therapist. The client's focus on the animal may result in easier articulation of thoughts and words because animals appear to be sympathetic listeners and cannot tell secrets. • Transfer the improved social interaction skills to family and peers.
Increase socialization and participation (individual or group).	• Prepare a scrapbook of photos, information, or articles about a specific dog breed and share the information with others. • Document attendance in therapy groups to determine if it increases when an animal is present.
Improve relationships with peers.	• Use the relationships between the handler and the animal and between the therapist and the animal as a metaphor for human relationships. • Work at transferring this experience to peers.
Increase amount of eye contact	• Work with the human-animal team to develop appropriate eye contact.

TREATMENT GOALS	AAT STRATEGY
with people.	• Work at transferring that skill to other relationships.
Improve appropriateness of voice tone with people.	• Work with the human-animal team to develop appropriate voice tone when training the animal. • Work at transferring this skill to other relationships.
Improve Socialization, Communication.	Practice teaching an animal something new.

Table 2: Example goals and strategies to facilitate bonding.

TREATMENT GOAL	AAT STRATEGY
Encourage bonding to a living being.	• Give the client a photograph of themselves and the companion animal to help strengthen the bond between sessions. • Establish predictable routines for greeting and saying goodbye to the animal at each session.
Acknowledgement of positive interactions.	• Observe the animal's recognition of the client at each session. • Observe and interpret the animal's happiness to see the client for each session.
Encouraging nurturing behavior.	Allow client to nurture the animal with appropriate rewards and affection.
Improve ability to trust.	• Interact with and learn about the animal and its behaviors. • Talk to the animal. • Receive affection from the animal.

TREATMENT GOAL	AAT STRATEGY
Learn about appropriate touch.	• Observe and discuss the animal's response to human touch. • Learn gentle ways to handle the animal. • Receive apparent acceptance from the animal. • Give appropriate affection to the animal. • Compare appropriate animal touch to appropriate human touch. • Forecast "what would happen if...?"
Distract from discomfort and pain (emotional or physical).	• Focus the discussion on the animal, rather than the client.

Table 3: Example goals and strategies to address emotions.

TREATMENT GOAL	AAT STRATEGY
Openly discuss feelings.	• Talk about traumatic events in the animal's life (e.g., being taken from its parents and siblings, going to live in a stranger's home, losing an owner due to illness, staying at a boarding kennel, getting in a fight with another animal), and ask the client to describe how the animal may have felt during these events. • Ask the client how they would feel if they were faced with similar situations. • Encourage the client to talk about their feelings through the animal. • Ask the client to interpret the animal's emotions as they occur. • Learn about animal emotions.

TREATMENT GOAL	AAT STRATEGY
	• Observe and discuss the animal's response to human emotions. • Use pictures of feeling faces (animals and people) to make a game out of identifying emotions that are depicted in the pictures. Talk about what events might have resulted in those feelings. Give bonus points if the clients can identify their own negative self-beliefs and then state rational contradictions to these beliefs. This may work well in groups.
Improve verbal expression.	Ask the client to answer questions about the animal (express opinions).
Differentiate between comfortable and uncomfortable feelings.	• Talk about events in the animal's life, and ask the client to determine if the animal likely felt comfortable or uncomfortable during these situations. • Ask the client how they would feel if they were faced with similar situations. • Transfer this information to relevant situations in the client's life.
Identify different emotions.	• Observe and interact with the animal. • Ask the client to describe what the animal may be feeling in a variety of situations (e.g., excited to see them, eager to do a trick, bored by repetitive activity, ecstatic to see a toy, frustrated if they cannot have something they want, uncertain about a new activity, frightened by a loud noise, tired after a run, disappointed about not being allowed to play).

TREATMENT GOAL	AAT STRATEGY
Learn about verbal and non-verbal expressions of feelings.	• Observe and discuss the animal's verbal and non-verbal expressions and what they mean. • Compare what is learned to human expressions.
Acquire socially acceptable ways of expressing feelings.	• Observe and interact with the animal. • Discuss the ways the animal expresses its feelings and what behaviors the client finds acceptable (e.g., prancing, wagging tail) or unacceptable (e.g., licking face, barking). • Discuss self-control and how to regulate behaviors in human relationships and experiences.
Recognize how others are feeling.	• Observe and interact with the animal. • Ask the client to describe what the animal may be feeling. • Transfer this to the human situation.

Table 4: Example goals and strategies for promoting empathy.

TREATMENT GOAL	AAT STRATEGY
Demonstrate appropriate nurturing behavior.	Observe and discuss appropriate nurturing behavior with the animal. Observe humane animal handling techniques. Observe the loving bond between the animal and the handler. Transfer these observations to human situations.
Demonstrate appropriate correction techniques.	Observe the animal making mistakes and the correction techniques used to handle the mistakes. Discuss these observations. Observe and discuss the empathy that the handler has for the animal.
Demonstrate patience and understanding.	Teach the animal something new or try to get the animal to respond to obedience commands given by the client. Encourage

TREATMENT GOAL	AAT STRATEGY
	patience and teach the client how to get successful results.

Table 5: Example goals and strategies to build self-esteem.

TREATMENT GOALS	AAT STRATEGY
Increase sense of purpose.	• Provide care for the animal (e.g., walk, brush). • Research options for getting a companion animal after discharge.
Increase self-esteem through learning a new skill or re-learning/adapting a skill to previous status.	• Learn how to teach the animal something by first learning how to treat the animal with respect, developing a relationship with the animal, developing observation and listening skills, learning proper praising techniques, learning to be tolerant of mistakes (their own and the animal's), and recognizing their progress. • Practice what is learned over a series of sessions. • Share the new skill with others. • Re-acquire an old skill (e.g., braid a rope that can be used as a leash for the animal, throw a ball).
Improve self-confidence.	• Have the client earn the respect and trust of the animal over time so that the animal will respond to the client's instructions. • Provide care (food, water, brushing) for the companion animal. • Receive recognition and attention from the animal.
Improve self-	• Receive apparent affection from the

TREATMENT GOALS	AAT STRATEGY
image	animal. • Have positive interactions with the animal.

Table 6: Example goals and strategies to promote 'giving' behavior.

TREATMENT GOAL	AAT STRATEGY
Learn about appropriate touch.	• Observe and discuss the animal's response to human touch. • Learn gentle ways to handle the animal. • Receive apparent acceptance from the animal. • Give affection to the animal. • Generalize the animal's behavior to human circumstances.
Decrease self-talk and recognize the needs of others.	• Work with the human-animal team to determine the needs of the animal. • Discuss the importance of meeting the animal's needs. • Determine what might happen if the animal's needs were not met. • Transfer this information to other situations.

Table 7: Example goals and strategies for enhancing personal growth and development.

TREATMENT GOAL	AAT STRATEGY
Increase leisure awareness and lifestyle choices.	• Learn about proper animal care. • Compare animal and human care. • Discuss possible changes that would improve the client's lifestyle.
Increase vocabulary.	• Learn new words relating to different dog breeds, obedience commands, animal characteristics, etc.

TREATMENT GOAL	AAT STRATEGY
	• Read or talk to the animal.
Stimulate interest, desire for knowledge.	• Give the client a project relating to an animal they are interested in. • Allow the client to share information with their peers.

Table 8: Example goals and strategies to provide a sense of control.

TREATMENT GOAL	AAT STRATEGY
Teach the animal a new trick or obedience command.	Learn how to teach the animal something by first learning how to treat the animal with respect, developing a relationship with the animal, developing observation and listening skills, learning proper praising techniques, learning to be tolerant of mistakes (their own and the animal's), and recognizing their progress.
Increase assertiveness as shown/measured by _____.	Practice role-playing assertive responses, with the animal as either an antagonist or a victim needing protection. Practice non verbal assertion (tone of voice, eye contact, body posture).

Table 9: Example goals and strategies for reducing abusive thoughts and behaviors.

TREATMENT GOAL	AAT STRATEGY
Promote empathy for living beings.	• Learn about and interact with the animal. • Discuss the animal's feelings in a variety of situations. • Compare the animal's feelings to human emotions.

TREATMENT GOAL	AAT STRATEGY
Decrease negative comments and increase positive comments.	• Work with the human-animal team to learn appropriate praising techniques. • Directly confront this issue, using the animal as an example, and transfer it to other situations.
Decrease abusive tendencies.	• Observe and discuss compassion and understanding within the human-animal team. • Observe and discuss appropriate ways to address frustration or anger. • Learn about and then assist in the care/grooming/feeding of an animal. • Learn about animal emotions. • Discuss how animals might feel if they are neglected or abused (relate to client's circumstances). • Transfer these observations to relevant situations in the client's life.
Decrease anger outbursts and increase appropriate reactions to frustration.	• When situations of frustration or nonsuccess arise while working with the human-animal team, use the opportunity to confront inappropriate or appropriate reactions. • Reinforce appropriate responses to frustration and nonsuccess. • Transfer the observations to relevant situations in the client's life.
Decrease manipulative behaviors.	• Observe the animal's behaviors. • Learn about the meaning of animal behavior(s). • Observe and discuss the animal's response to human behavior (immediate consequences). • Generalize animal behavior to human circumstances. • Practice teaching an animal something

TREATMENT GOAL	AAT STRATEGY
	new.
	• Develop a cooperative plan to accomplish something with an animal.
	• Forecast "what would happen if...?"
	• Engage in play with an animal.
Improve cooperation.	• Learn about and then assist in the care/grooming/feeding of an animal.
	• Develop a cooperative plan to accomplish something with the animal.

Table 10: Example goals and strategies to address mental health concerns.

TREATMENT GOALS	AAT STRATEGY
Anxiety	
Decrease symptoms of anxiety or agitation.	• Hold or stoke the companion animal while interacting with the therapist or the therapy group.
	• Talk to the animal.
	• Receive affection from the animal.
Improve ability to relax using diaphragmatic breathing and relaxation techniques.	• Observe how a relaxed animal rests and breathes.
	• Practice imitating the animal while imagining stressful situations in anxiety hierarchy (desensitization).
Identify and reduce irrational thoughts which trigger or exacerbate anxiety.	• Discuss possible origin and symptoms of the animal's irrational fears (e.g., thunder) and relate to client's fears when possible.
	• Have client consider the origins of his own anxiety or phobia, and identify the thoughts and sensations that

TREATMENT GOALS	AAT STRATEGY
	trigger anxiety.
	• Have client explain why the animal need not be afraid. Help client develop coping self-statements for his own situation.
	• If client is a child, ask child to help animal confront fears with rational and more positive beliefs. A card game that matches irrational thoughts with the best counter ideas could be developed.
Reduce avoidance of anxiety-provoking situations, places, groups, etc.	• While client pets the animal, use guided imagery to desensitize fears (e.g., confrontations, using elevators, giving a speech, taking a test successfully, sleeping alone in the dark).
	• Have animal accompany the client while they face some fears.
Increase assertiveness as shown/measured by:_____.	• Discuss fight or flight reactions in animals (cowering vs. aggression) and apply to people.
	• Practice role-playing with the animal taking various roles.
	• Practice process of gradually getting the animal to approach something it initially fears.
Identify and modify lifestyle variables which increase stress.	• Discuss stressors on animals and people (e.g., excess noise, not eating or sleeping well, arguments, losses), and

TREATMENT GOALS	AAT STRATEGY
	how these situations could be improved.
Reduce frequency of worrying, apprehension and avoidance tactics.	• Write/tell stories (related to client's own anxiety and worries) about a dog or other animal that overcomes its fears by facing them and discovering they are not real. • If client is a child, have them illustrate the story.
Reduce secondary symptoms of anxiety (e.g,restlessness, fatigue, irritability, stomach aches, sleep disturbances)	• Include client's symptoms in above stories with ways to reduce them. • If client is a child, have them exercise/play hard with animal, then practice relaxing while petting animal and imagining relaxing scenes together.
Depression	
Brighten affect and mood.	• Hold or stroke the companion animal while interacting with the therapist or the therapy group. • Teach the animal to do a trick, or engage in play with the animal.
Decrease learned helplessness behaviors. Increase sense of control over self and environment.	• Work with the human-animal team to effectively command the animal and to problem-solve when it does not respond correctly. • Directly confront this issue, using the animal as an example, and transfer it to other situations.
Reduce isolation, boredom, loneliness.	• Engage in play with the

TREATMENT GOALS	AAT STRATEGY
	animal. • Learn about and then assist in the care/grooming/feeding of the animal. • Reminisce about the past. • Remember and repeat information about the animal. • Learn about the animal, then introduce the animal to peers. • Take the animal for a walk. • Receive apparent acceptance from the animal. • Give appropriate affection to the animal.
Decrease feelings of worthlessness.	• Provide pleasure for or affection to the animal. • Spend time caring for/grooming the animal. • Take the animal for a walk, play its favorite game (e.g., fetch).
Address Grieving/Loss Issues.	• Talk about animals the person has known. • Reminisce about past animal loss(es). • Discuss how animals might feel when their animal companion dies, when baby animals leave their mothers, etc. • Transfer this to the human situation.
Reduce suicidal ideation/behavior	• Ask: "If the animal were to die suddenly, what impact would his death have on those who love him? What impact would YOUR suicide

TREATMENT GOALS	AAT STRATEGY
	have on your family and friends?" • Reflect on the animal's total self-acceptance without shame, without judging or comparing himself to others. • If the client is a child, talk about how the animal has suffered a loss similar to the child's. Discuss how the animal might feel sad, hopeless, or guilty and what could be done to help the animal feel better. • Discuss how the animal could that he was feeling better. Apply to the child.
Increase positive mood, attitudes for a period of ____ consecutive weeks.	• Consider the simple things that make animals/people happy. • Engage in some of those activities. • Have client keep a 'Pleasure Journal' of small, enjoyable events. • Ask clients about their future and what will make them happy? If client is a child, ask them to draw a picture of her/himself in the future.
Improve reality-testing and orientation (reduce dissociation, self-mutilation, etc.).	• Have client touch or stroke animal to help ground them in the present. • Have client describe the animal objectively in terms of their appearance, needs, activities, where the animal is now, what month it is, etc.

TREATMENT GOALS	AAT STRATEGY
Increase energy, initiative, and activity level.	• Play actively with the animal, take animal on regular walks (either client's own animal or therapist's/handler's). • Have client plan and teach the animal a new trick.
Increase assertion.	• Have client obedience-train their own animal. • Compare the ways animals and people react to an assertive tone of voice, to "no", to positive reinforcement, etc.
Improve decision-making and concentration.	• Ask client what to do about a problematic behavior of the animal's (parallel to client's behavior when possible). • Plan short-term goals and steps toward reaching goals. • Apply process to client's situation. • If client is a child, allow the child to decide what food treat to give the animal, which game to play, or when the animal needs to go out. • If client is a child, play "Simon Says" and "Mother May I?" using the animal's name (e.g., Rufus says...) or the child's name (e.g., Jill says...Sit).

TREATMENT GOALS	AAT STRATEGY
Reduce irrational thoughts that increase or maintain depression.	• Discuss the client's (or animal's) negative self-beliefs (e.g., I can't do anything right, nobody likes me). • Practice contradicting with rational statements. • As evidence to refute client's irrational thoughts, point out the animal's affection and loyalty to client despite past mistakes, imperfections, etc.
Increase social interaction.	• Have client interpret the animal's feelings based on the animal's behavior. • Ask the client to talk about their own feelings and behaviors in similar circumstances. • In groups, have group members take turns throwing a ball for the animal or demonstrating tricks the animal has learned to do. • Discuss amazing animal tales or feats.
Get an adequate amount of restorative sleep most nights for a period of _____	• Client observes how relaxed the animal is and how it breathes deeply. Practice similar breathing techniques while visualizing relaxing dream images for the client (or animal). • Try the same technique at night.

TREATMENT GOALS	AAT STRATEGY
Increase interest and participation in daily activities.	• Monitor attendance and interaction at AAT sessions. • Talk about the client's daily activities and determine what may make them more fun. • Note how frequently the client smiles at or pets the animal.
Improve appetite most days for a period of ____ consecutive weeks.	• Point out character flaws or flaws in physical appearance of the animal and how they do not affect the animal's self-image. Work on translating this to clients who have problems with their own self-image. • If client is a child, have a tea party where the child feeds the animal and him/herself. • Play "red light-green light" when eating meals.
Attention-Deficit Hyperactivity	
Improve attention/concentration.	• Teach the animal a trick or an obedience command. • Transfer success in activities with the companion animal to treatment activities and daily living activities.

TREATMENT GOALS	AAT STRATEGY
Decrease distractibility.	• Work with the human-animal team to help maintain concentration on the work with the animal when giving commands or teaching a trick. • Directly confront this issue, using the animal as an example, and transfer it to other situations.
Improve memory (short-term or long-term) or recall.	• Recall information about the animal (name, age, color, etc.). • Reminisce about animals the person knew or had in the past. • Remember details about the animal and the animal's care. • Describe the animal when it is not present. • Follow a sequence of instructions with the animal.
Improve Reality Orientation.	• Take the animal around and introduce it to others. • Interact with (pet, play, talk to, groom, etc.) the animal. • Give affection to and receive affection from the animal. • Reminisce about the past. • Remember and repeat information about the animal. • Describe the animal.

TREATMENT GOALS	AAT STRATEGY
Decrease self-talk relating to the fantasy world.	• Work with the human-animal team to emphasize the importance of staying focused on the "here and now" with the animal when giving commands. • Directly confront this issue, using the animal as an example, and transfer it to other situations.

A therapists' checklist for selecting appropriate AAT clients

☐ Select an appropriate client for AAT, complete client suitability questionnaire

☐ Ensure there are no contraindications (fear, allergies, etc.)

☐ Ensure there are no current aggression issues or history of animal abuse

☐ Ask the client if they would like to join the program

☐ Have the client or their guardian sign a waiver allowing them to participate in the AAT program

☐ Have the client or their guardian sign a waiver allowing the client to complete the evaluations (Professional/client information release consent)

☐ Assign the client an ID. Either use therapists' initials, followed by the number according to the order they began therapy, (i.e., Bill Frank's first client would be BF1; Sue Andersons third client would be SA3), or use the facility name's first letter, followed by the client's initials, (i.e., Yellowhead Youth Center's client, Andrew Marz, would be Y-AM)

☐ Using the Session Planning Worksheet:
  ▪ Assess what problems the client has that can be addressed using AAT
  ▪ Determine what goals may help to alleviate those problems (short- and long-term)
  ▪ Plan what strategies/activities to use to attain those goals

☐ Proceed with the session!

☐ Have the client complete the client questionnaire

☐ Complete the therapist questionnaire

☐ Plan the next session

The Chimo Project: AAT Intervention Planning
WORKSHEET

Symptom/ Deficit

Treatment Goal

Treatment Strategy

Was the Treatment Successful?

THERAPY ANIMAL BEHAVIOR INVENTORY			
Therapy Animal Name:		Handler:	

BASIC BEHAVIOR (use check mark)					ADVANCED BEHAVIOR
Walks politely on leash					Learned new trick
Recognized client at the beginning of the session					Tugs
Sits/Stays		On leash		Off leash	Holds objects in mouth
Downs /Stays		On leash		Off leash	Picks up/retrieves objects on command
Did trick for client					Plays fetch/plays with toy
Comes to/sits with person (off leash)					Demonstrates empathetic response
Sits/lies/stays with client for petting					Sits/lies/stays with client without petting
Brushed by client					Made a mistake (client frustrated, or handler corrected humanely)
Took treat from client					Other:

168

The Chimo Project: AAT Session Tracking Sheet

Animal-Assisted Therapy Program with _____

AAT Session Tracking Sheet

Therapy Date	Session Duration	Therapist Name	Client ID (Therapist Init. & Client # or facility # & Client Init)	AAT Session # for Client 000X	Therapy Type (indiv; grp; schl)	Animal Handler Name	Questinnaire & Tracking		
							Date Filled		Date Submitted
							Therapist	Client	

Animal-Assisted Therapy
CLIENT REFERRAL FORM

Client Name:	Therapist:

Diagnosis:

Precautions:

Pertinent History: Please check all that apply

_____ Physically abused   _____ Traumatic history

_____ Suicide attempt(s)   _____ Poor impulse control

_____ Animal abuse   _____ Has had pets

_____ Other (briefly specify)

Symptoms: Please check all that apply

_____ Depression   _____ Withdrawn

_____ Anxiety   _____ Poor play skills

_____ High blood pressure   _____ Bland affect

_____ Poor short-term memory   _____ Uncommunicative

_____ Inappropriate touching   _____ Poor concentration

_____ Sexually preoccupied   _____ Religiously preoccupied

_____ Poor socialization skills   _____ Physically inactive/ sedentary

_____ Lack of engagement in unit activities   _____ Hyperactive

_____ Difficulty adjusting to hospital environment

_____ Delusions (briefly specify):

_____ Hallucinations (briefly specify):

_____ Other (briefly specify):

AAT INCIDENT REPORT FORM

Date of Incident:		Time:	
Place of Incident:		Client:	
Therapist:		Volunteer:	
Witness(es):			
Animal's Name:		Species:	

How did the incident happen? (Who, What, When, Where, Why, How?)

_____

_____

_____

_____

_____

_____

Was anyone hurt? (circle one)	YES	NO
Was first aid given? (circle one)	YES	NO
Did the injured person resume his/her activities? (If no, please explain)	YES	NO
Was further medical treatment required? (circle one)	YES	NO
Did/does client need to consult with a doctor? (circle one)	YES	NO

Volunteer's Signature	Injured Individual's Signature
AAT/AAA Coordinator's Signature	Witness's Signature

Animal-Assisted Therapy
Waiver Release and Indemnity

Animal-Assisted Therapy

This is to inform you that your child may have the opportunity to interact and work with animals that are part of Animal-Assisted Therapy (AAT) at _____. Eligibility and appropriateness to participate in AAT will be assessed by the treatment team.

AAT is a goal-directed therapeutic intervention that focuses on helping children discover parts of themselves through interacting with a skilled animal and a _____ staff member who is skilled in human-animal interactions. AAT is an opportunity for children to let down their guard, increase their motivation, develop trust, and feel good about themselves. The animal will be accompanied by an owner at all times. Although all animals used in AAT are carefully screened for good health, obedience skills, and aptitude, in any activity there are inherent risks. We require your permission to allow the client to participate in AAT, if deemed appropriate.

Please Initial the Following Three Sections

Initial Box

I, the undersigned, understand and acknowledge that I am aware of the risks associated with or related to the use of AAT (including the risk of severe or fatal injury) to my child or child for whom I am responsible. These risk particulars may include but are not limited to the following:
   a) injuries resulting from animal scratches
   b) injuries resulting from allergic responses to animals
   c) injuries resulting from animal nips or bites

d) potentially serious injuries resulting from any
physical contact with an animal.

Initial Box

[   ]

I understand that by signing this document, my
successors, heirs, assigns or personal representative
waive the right to sue or otherwise claim against
_____ or its employees, directors, agents,
volunteers, affiliates, or independent contractors for any
loss or damage connected with any property loss or
personal injury that is sustained while participating in or
preparing for any program or activity of the
_____. I fully understand clearly that my
successors, heirs, assigns and personal representatives
waive the right to sue or otherwise claim against
_____ or its employees, directors, agents,
volunteers, affiliates, or independent contractors if the
loss or injury suffered results wholly or in part of the
negligence of _____, its employees,
directors, agents, volunteers, affiliates, or independent
contractors, or from the negligence of any third party,
including other participants in the program.

Initial Box

[   ]

I further agree to indemnify and save harmless
_____, employees, directors, agents,
affiliates, volunteers, or independent contractors from
any and all actions, claims, demands, losses or suits of
any nature resulting from and rising from my
participation in any program in The _____
or my use of its facilities or from the participation of my
child or child for whom I am responsible in any program
in _____ or from that child's use of its facilities.

Client (Participant in AAT)

Name: _____

Date of Birth: _____ / _____ / _____

Address: _____

Phone Number: _____

Contact in case of Emergency: _____

Phone Number: _____

Parent/Guardian of Client (Participant in AAT)

Name: _____

Phone Number: _____

Address: _____

Alternate Phone Number: _____

2nd Emergency Contact: _____

Phone Number: _____

INTERACTION WITH AN ANIMAL IS A COMPONENT OF ANIMAL-ASSISTED THERAPY

I acknowledge that I have read and fully understood this agreement prior to signature.

I WITNESS THAT I have executed this document at the City of

_____ in the province of _____ this _____ day

of _____, 20____.

_____
Signature of Parent/Guardian (for Participant Under 18)

Witness: _____ **Staff Member**

Name: _____

Signature of Witness _____

Date: _____

Animal-Assisted Therapy Professional/Client Information Release Consent

Dated in the City of _____

this _____ day of _____, 20____

Due to the delicate nature of our Animal-Assisted Therapy programs, and in order to fulfill our responsibility to our funding organizations and our volunteer clients, it is necessary that we obtain information regarding treatment. The information will be kept in the strictest of confidence. We, the undersigned, hereby authorize _____
to receive information regarding the client's background, medical conditions, and services provided.

Client's Name _____
(Print)   Mr./Ms/Miss   First Name   Last Name

Date of Birth _____
(Print)   Month / Date / Year

_____

Guardian Name: _____
Address: _____
Phone: _____
Fax: _____

I hereby authorize _____ to
obtain/release information to/from:

_____

_____

Witness Name   **Applicant Name**

(Print) Mr./Ms/Miss -- First Name -- Last Name

Signature   Signature

Address   Address

This consent is valid:

___ _From the date signed until_ _____

___ _Until discharge and/or withdrawal from programs, whichever comes first._

Animal-Assisted Therapy
Volunteer Release Form

Dated in the City of _____ this _____ day of _____, 20___

In consideration of being permitted to participate as a volunteer in a program organized or authorized by _____, I the undersigned, agree to assume all risk of injury, including death to myself or my animal, or damage to my property while participating in the _____ programs. I hereby waive any right of action I may have had or may in the future lodge against the _____, its originating or participating organizations, assigns, directors, staff, agents, or volunteers for any such loss or injury caused by negligence or default of _____, its originating or participating organizations, their successors, assigns, directors, staff, agents, or volunteers. I hereby waive for myself, my animal, my personal representatives and dependants all such claims or rights of action aforementioned. By my signature, I acknowledge that I am of full age and that I have read this release and have voluntarily signed it.

_____   _____
Witness Name   **Applicant Name**
(Print) Mr./Ms/Miss -- First Name -- Last Name

_____   _____
Signature   Signature

Address   Address

_____   _____
_____   _____
_____   _____

Assigned Professional:

_____

(print) Title -- First Name -- Last Name

_____

(Job / Position)

Authorized by:

_____

(print) Title -- First Name -- Last Name

_____

(Signature)

Date: _____

Animal-Assisted Therapy
Volunteer Confidentiality Agreement

Dated in the City of _____ this _____ day of
_____, 20___

Between:

_____

And

_____
Applicant (print)   Mr./Ms/Miss -- First Name -- Last Name

I understand that in the course of my volunteer work I may be exposed to information of a confidential nature and pertaining to clients and/or their families.

I will consider as confidential all information which I may hear directly or indirectly. I will not seek information in regard to a client, except as it pertains to my volunteer assignment. I will not release or discuss with anyone information about clients or their families.

I will uphold the standards of _____
and will safeguard its reputation by maintaining the highest standard of confidentiality.

_____	_____
Witness Name	**Applicant Name**
(Print) Mr./Ms/Miss -- First Name -- Last Name	
_____	_____
Signature	Signature
Address	Address
_____	_____
_____	_____
_____	_____

Assigned Professional:

_____
(print) Title -- First Name -- Last Name

_____
(Job / Position)

Authorized by:

_____
(print) Title -- First Name -- Last Name

_____
(Signature)

Date: _____

Therapist Questionnaire
ANIMAL-ASSISTED THERAPY (AAT)

Please fill out one questionnaire per client after AAT is used in a session.

A. General Information
* Indicates mandatory questions to be completed each time the questionnaire is done.

*1. Therapy session date: ____/_____/____ (Month/Day/Year)

*2. Client's ID number (and therapist initial): _____

*3a. Client's birth date: ____/_____/____ (Month/Day/Year)
*3b. Child's gender: _____
*3c. Client's presenting diagnoses: _____

_____

_____

_____

*4. How long (approximately) have you been seeing this client?

_____

*5. Therapy type used with AAT animal today
(group/individual/class): _____

*6. Length of AAT session today: _____

*7. Animal handler first name: _____

*8. Your name: _____

Fill in the following section only on your first submission
9. Your role/position: _____

10a. Your age: _____   10b. Your gender: _____

11. Have you ever had a pet?   ☐ Yes   ☐ No

   If yes, what kind?   ☐ dog   ☐ cat   ☐ other
   (specify) _____

12. Do you have a pet now?   ☐ Yes   ☐ No

If yes, what kind? ☐ dog ☐cat ☐ other
(specify) _____

13. Have you ever worked with an animal in AAT before?

☐ Yes ☐No

Comments:

_____

_____

_____

_____

B. Specific Information about the Client

Each of these questions describes your client's behavior during **today's session with the animal**.

Circle the number (or "n/a") that reflects your level of agreement with each of the following:	Not at all in the session	A few times in the session	Often in the session	Quite a bit in the session	Constantly in the session	Not /Appl. or cannot tell
1. The client was comfortable talking with me.	0	1	2	3	4	n/a c/t
2. The client was able to focus on important problems when talking with me.	0	1	2	3	4	n/a c/t
3. The client looked forward to coming to (e.g. group, therapy, class)	0	1	2	3	4	n/a c/t
4. The client would have liked _____ (e.g., group, therapy, class) to last longer.	0	1	2	3	4	n/a c/t
5. The client was willing to discuss what is happening to important people in his/her life.	0	1	2	3	4	n/a c/t
6. The client was willing to talk about his/her feelings during _____ (e.g., group, therapy, class)	0	1	2	3	4	n/a c/t

		Strongly Disagree	→				Strongly Agree	Not /Appl. or cannot tell

7. As a result of work done with the client, he/she is more hopeful about his/her life. 0 1 2 3 4 n/a c/t

8. The client's mood has improved because of the work done today. 0 1 2 3 4 n/a c/t

C. Overall Assessment of the _____-Chimo Project AAT Treatment Effect

Based on feedback from your colleagues and the client's family/guardians, **circle** the answer that reflects your level of agreement with each of the following:

		Strongly Disagree	→				Strongly Agree	Not /Appl. or cannot tell

1. I feel that the AAT work with the client helps him/her to perform better with his/her <u>peers</u>. 0 1 2 3 4 n/a c/t

2. I feel that the AAT work with the client helps him/her to perform better with the <u>child care staff</u>. 0 1 2 3 4 n/a c/t

3. I feel that the AAT work with the client helps him/her to perform better with his/her <u>family/guardians</u>. 0 1 2 3 4 n/a c/t

4. I feel that the AAT work with the client helps him/her to perform better with <u>tasks</u> at _____. 0 1 2 3 4 n/a c/t

5. I feel that the AAT work with the client helps him/her to perform better <u>educationally.</u> 0 1 2 3 4 n/a c/t

	Strongly Disagree		→		Strongly Agree	Not /Appl. or cannot tell
6. I feel that the AAT work with the client helps him/her to perform better overall <u>socially</u>.	0	1	2	3	4	n/a c/t
7. I feel that the AAT work with the client helps his/her <u>overall mood</u> after the sessions and for the next few hours.	0	1	2	3	4	n/a c/t
8. I feel that the AAT work with the client helps his/her <u>overall behavior</u> after the sessions and for the next few hours.	0	1	2	3	4	n/a c/t

D. Specific Information about the Animal

Each of these questions describes <u>your client's behavior during</u> **today's session with the animal**.   **Circle** the number (or "n/a") that reflects your level of agreement with each of the following:

	Not at all in the session	A few times in the session	Often in the session	Quite a bit in the session	Constantly in the session	Not Applicable or Cannot Tell
1. The client settled faster when the animal was present.	0	1	2	3	4	n/a c/t
2. The animal's presence seemed to make the client more willing to come to (e.g. group, therapy, class)	0	1	2	3	4	n/a c/t
3. The animal served as a source of comfort for the client.	0	1	2	3	4	n/a c/t
4. The animal provided impetus to discuss attachment issues with the client.	0	1	2	3	4	n/a c/t

	Not at all in the session	A few times in the session	Often in the session	Quite a bit in the session	Constantly in the session	Not Applicable or Cannot Tell
5. The animal's presence helped the client want to stay longer.	0	1	2	3	4	n/a c/t
6. The client was more open as a result of the animal's presence.	0	1	2	3	4	n/a c/t
7. The animal's presence helped the client to discuss positive feelings.	0	1	2	3	4	n/a c/t
8. The client paid more attention to the animal than to the therapist/teacher.	0	1	2	3	4	n/a c/t
9. The client was distracted by the animal and unable to focus on clinically relevant issues.	0	1	2	3	4	n/a c/t
10. The client was more communicative in the presence of the animal.	0	1	2	3	4	n/a c/t
11. The client exhibited aggressive behaviors towards the animal.	0	1	2	3	4	n/a c/t
12. The client touched the animal.	0	1	2	3	4	n/a c/t
13. The client talked directly to the animal.	0	1	2	3	4	n/a c/t
14. The client was more willing to disclose as a result of the animal's presence.	0	1	2	3	4	n/a c/t
15. The client was unable to focus on clinically relevant issues as a result of the animal's presence.	0	1	2	3	4	n/a c/t

16. Do you notice more empathetic behaviour when the animal is present? ☐ Yes ☐ No

_____

_____

17a. Do you notice improved social skills when the animal is present? ☐ Yes ☐ No

17b. If yes, do these effects persist when the animal is absent?

_____

_____

E. Animal Handler Presence in Session

The following section is to be completed <u>only</u> if an <u>animal handler</u> (e.g., child care worker and his/her dog, or volunteer handler and his/her dog) <u>was in the therapy session/class</u> with you and the client.

	Strongly Disagree				Strongly Agree	Not /Appl. or cannot tell
18. I felt comfortable having the <u>animal handler</u> in the room.	0	1	2	3	4	n/a c/t
19. Having the <u>animal handler</u> in the room did not change the way I felt when talking to the client.	0	1	2	3	4	n/a c/t
20. Having the <u>animal handler</u> in the room did not change the way the client talks to me.	0	1	2	3	4	n/a c/t

F. Goal Attainment

21. How the animal was used to meet the treatment goals.

_____

_____

_____

_____

G. Comments

_____

_____

_____

_____

_____

_____

Client Questionnaire
Animal-Assisted Therapy (AAT)

Please fill out a questionnaire each week after attending Animal-Assisted Therapy sessions. *Your name and identity will be kept strictly confidential. Any data reported will be in a group summary format.*

A. General Information

1. Today's date: _____/_____/_____ (Day/Month/Year)
2. Your client number(?): _____
3a. Your age: _____   3b. Your gender: _____
4. Have you ever had a pet?   ☐ Yes   ☐ No

   If yes, what kind?   ☐ Dog   ☐ Cat   ☐ Other
   (please specify) _____

5. Do you have a pet now?   ☐ Yes   ☐ No

   If yes, what kind?   ☐ Dog   ☐ Cat   ☐ Other
   (please specify) _____

6. When you are sad, who do you talk to? _____

_____

B. Overall Assessment
For each of the items below, **check** the picture that describes how you feel.

1. The animal helps me to concentrate or finish my work at school.	☐ ☐ ☐ ☐
	Not at all A Lot

2.	The animal helps me to stay on good behavior in my _____ house.	☐ ☐ ☐ ☐ Not A Lot at all
3.	The animal helps me to do my assigned tasks at my _____ house.	☐ ☐ ☐ ☐ Not A Lot at all

C. Specific Information about the Animal

For each of the items below, **check** the picture that describes how you feel.

1.	The animal helped me feel good about myself.	☐ ☐ ☐ ☐ Not A Lot at all
2.	The animal helped me feel more comfortable with my therapist.	☐ ☐ ☐ ☐ Not A Lot at all
3.	I could focus better when the animal was there.	☐ ☐ ☐ ☐ Not A Lot at all
4.	I like _____ better with the animal (e.g., group, class, therapy, _____ house)	☐ ☐ ☐ ☐ Not A Lot at all
5.	I want to go to _____ more when the animal is there (e.g. group, class, therapy, _____ house).	☐ ☐ ☐ ☐ Not A Lot at all

6. It was easier to talk about my problems when the animal was there.	☐ ☐ ☐ ☐ Not A Lot at all
7. It was easier to talk openly about my feelings when the animal was there.	☐ ☐ ☐ ☐ Not A Lot at all
8. The animal liked me.	☐ ☐ ☐ ☐ Not A Lot at all
9. I felt good when I was with the animal.	☐ ☐ ☐ ☐ Not A Lot at all
10. I sometimes cannot concentrate when the animal is there.	☐ ☐ ☐ ☐ Not A Lot at all

11a. Do you think the animal helps you? ☐ Yes ☐ No

11b. If yes, what does the animal help you do?

_____

_____

_____

_____

D. Animal Handler Information
The following section is to be completed only if an animal handler and his/her animal was present in the therapy session/class/_____ house.

1. I felt comfortable having the animal handler in the room (eg. group, class, therapy, _____ house) when I was talking to my therapist or teacher.	☐ ☐ ☐ ☐ Not at all ⟶ A Lot
2. Having the animal handler in the room changed the way I talked with my therapist or teacher (eg. group, class, therapy, _____ house).	☐ ☐ ☐ ☐ Not at all ⟶ A Lot

E. Comments

1a. Do you like having animals work with you at _____ ?
☐ Yes   ☐ No

1b. Why?

_____
_____
_____
_____

Volunteer Boundary Information Form

It is important that therapists and volunteers are clear with each other about how to maintain proper boundaries with the client. This form is to be filled out by the therapist and given to the volunteer in order to facilitate clear communication. If the therapist is unclear about any of these items, they should consult their professional organization.

During the first introduction meeting			
☐ Speak whenever you like	☐ Answer questions	☐ Only answer questions about you or your animal	☐ Please do not speak
Before the session			
☐ Speak whenever you like	☐ Answer questions	☐ Only answer questions about you or your animal	☐ Please do not speak
During the session			
☐ Speak whenever you like	☐ Answer questions	☐ Only answer questions about you or your animal	☐ Please do not speak
After the session			
☐ Speak whenever you like	☐ Answer questions	☐ Only answer questions about you or your animal	☐ Please do not speak
Outside the sessions			
☐ Feel free to have contacts/meetings	☐ Inform me of meetings you have	☐ Ask me before you meet with the client	☐ Please do not contact/meet the client

Sensitive Subjects (please avoid the topics with checked boxes)

☐ Any identifying information about yourself (address, phone number, area of town, school, work, etc.)	☐ If they have made any friends at the facility	☐ The client's family
☐ How their progress is going	☐ Holidays	☐ Your family
☐ How they like their treatment	☐ The client's animals	☐ Movies
☐ How they like the facility	☐ Television	☐ Other (explain)

If you see the client outside therapy sessions, feel free to:

Make eye contact	☐ Yes	☐ No
Initiate a conversation	☐ Yes	☐ No
Speak to them if they approach you	☐ Yes	☐ No
Allow them to lead the conversation	☐ Yes	☐ No

Remember to be sensitive about the information you have about them

If you would like to talk about your experiences, please:

☑ Refrain from referring to the client by name
☐ Refrain from referring to the client's family/history
☐ Refrain from referring to the client's specific problem (ie. Do not refer to 'depression' but DO refer to, 'they were sad')
☐ Refrain from referring to the facility
☐ Refrain from referring to the therapist by name
☑ Please feel free to talk to anyone about the valuable volunteer work you are doing!

Comments:

STAFF ANIMAL SURVEY

The purpose of this survey is to determine the needs of staff that would like to bring their animals into _____ to participate in Animal-Assisted Therapy (AAT). The information you provide will be used as part of the planning process for implementation of the AAT program at _____.

When you have finished answering the questions, please return

the survey to _____ at _____.

Please return by _____

(Name)   (Location)

1. Your professional discipline: _____

2. Type/s of animal/s you have that you would like to participate in AAT at _____

   ❑ dog   Name:_____   Age:____
   ❑ cat   Name:_____   Age:____
   ❑ other, please specify_____
             Name:_____   Age:____

3. What would need to be in place at _____ to ensure that your animal's housing needs are met when he/she is not participating in therapy?

   ❑ indoor kennel
   Where could this be kept?_____

   ❑ empty room or office that locks
   Do you have a place in mind that would suit your needs?

   ❑ outdoor enclosed dog run and insulated kennel
   Location?   ❑ central so others can share the space
              ❑ close to my location
              ❑ other; please specify

4. What would need to be in place at _____ to ensure that your animal's toileting needs are met while he/she is at _____?

❑ designated outside toileting area and bin for disposal
Where could this be located?_____

❑ designated indoor space for litter box
Where could this be located?_____

❑ other, please specify _____

5. Would you require any special equipment to be available for your animal at _____? If so, please specify.

_____

6. Please read each of the following statements and mark the box that best reflects your opinion. If you would like to add additional comments, please do so in the space provided at the end of the question.

	Strongly Agree	Agree	Disagree	Strongly Disagree	Not Sure
a) My animal is people-oriented.	❑	❑	❑	❑	❑
b) My animal is sociable.	❑	❑	❑	❑	❑
c) My animal is comfortable being touched by strangers.	❑	❑	❑	❑	❑
d) My animal copes well with stressful situations.	❑	❑	❑	❑	❑
e) My animal is controllable, manageable, and predictable at all times.	❑	❑	❑	❑	❑
f) My animal is going to enjoy being a part of therapy.	❑	❑	❑	❑	❑

_____

_____

_____

_____

_____

_____

_____

7. Do you have any experience or training in AAT?

❑ educational
What programs/courses? _____

_____

_____

_____

❑ practical
How long ago did you start using AAT? _____

Are you currently using it?
❑ yes, on a regular basis
❑ yes, on an irregular basis
❑ no
❑ little to none

Thank you for your participation!

Dog Evaluation Exercises

To evaluate temperament, dogs must:

Accept the approach of a friendly stranger – This exercise provides the evaluator with information in order to determine the dog's level of acceptance of an unknown person approaching the handler in a natural, everyday situation.

The evaluator will greet the handler in a friendly manner, shake hands and ignore the dog, thereafter walking behind and around the dog/handler team. The dog is allowed to show interest/sniff the stranger, but not to jump up on them or become aggressively interested.

Accept petting – This exercise demonstrates that the dog will accept a non-threatening stranger touching it.

The evaluator will again approach the team, request permission to pet the dog, and proceed to touch the dog on its head and body.

Accept examination – Following petting, the evaluator will continue with an inspection of the dog by lightly handling the ears, teeth, and eyes, and gently picking up each front foot.

The dog may change position from a sit to a stand during the inspection phase, but may not show shyness or aggression. Dogs with medical conditions (such as ear infections, stitches or open wounds, etc.) are not suitable for testing. The handler should rebook when the dog is healthy.

To evaluate obedience:

The dog must demonstrate reliable responses to the commands including, "sit", "down", "stay", "come", "heel" and "settle."

The terms set out here are traditional obedience commands. If a dog has been trained to respond to different wording of these commands, they will be accepted. What we are looking for is the dog's response to the commands in a manner in which the handler delivers the commands, not what the command actually is.

We are not expecting competition-style obedience work, but we are expecting the dog to work on a loose, relaxed leash. Dogs are expected to work no further than three feet away from the handler at any given time and must not be guided or pulled by the leash.

Sit – With the dog standing beside the handler, the evaluator will instruct the handler to ask their dog to sit. The evaluator will be looking for the dog to sit. And maintain the sit command until given an additional command or release from the sit.

Down – The handler may choose to have the dog begin from a sitting or standing position. The evaluator will instruct the handler to give the command "down". The evaluator watches to see that the dog lies down without handling (luring without food is allowed). Once the dog is in the down position, it is expected that the dog will maintain the down position until an additional command or release is given.

Stay – Dogs are expected to maintain a fifteen (15) second sit/stay and a thirty (30) second down/stay with the handler at the end of the leash.

Come – On the instruction of the evaluator, the handler will be instructed to leave the dog in either a sit or down position and walk to a point approximately fifteen feet from the dog. Then, on instruction of the evaluator, the handler will be instructed to call the dog who is expected to come to the handler without any detours.

Heel – Dogs are expected to be able to walk politely beside their handlers on a loose leash as the handler walks in a variety of patterns with occasional stops and changes of direction. The dogs are not expected to sit when the handlers stop, but they are expected to wait quietly beside their handlers until the handlers resume walking. Patterns will include walking by people with walkers, wheelchairs and/or other distractions.

Additionally, items will be dropped while the handler/dog team is working. A dog may show interest and curiosity, and may be startled slightly, but should not panic.

Settle – This is the dog's ability to calm down promptly upon the handler's command following play. The handler may use any command as long as the dog quickly discontinues play, thereafter quietly waiting for further instructions from the handler.

To evaluate the dog's relationship with the handler:

Awareness of one another and interaction are important elements of a desirable bond between handler and dog. Demonstration of such interaction provides the evaluator with the information necessary to rate the team. Evaluators will be watching for positive interaction between the handler and dog. Handlers are encouraged to interact with their dog and offer encouragement at any time it is deemed appropriate or necessary. Praise and talking to the dog while the team is working is desirable. A dog should be aware of its handler and be responsive to the handler's spoken word and touch. A dog that ignores the handler demonstrates a weak bond. Likewise, a handler who is unaware of the dog's reaction to surroundings demonstrates the lack of a bond with the animal.

- The 'Relationship bonus' will be available on all exercises. A happy (not necessarily perfectly obedient) dog and handler who are enjoying the work will be awarded bonus points.

- Handler teams must complete (second and third attempts are also considered complete) all exercises to receive their qualification.

- There are four final designations. 'Pass with Flying Colors' is a completion of all exercises including scores for Relationship Bonus. 'Pass' is a dog who completed all the exercises. 'Failure – try again' is for dogs who did not complete all the exercises, or a dog with extreme shyness. 'Failure' is for a dog that exhibits high levels of aggression.

- If a dog exhibits aggressive behavior, they will receive a 'Failure Aggression'. It will be the judge's discretion as to whether the dog will be allowed to attempt the test again in the future.

- If a dog exhibits excessive shyness (such that the judge deems the dog to be in extreme discomfort), then the dog will receive a 'Failure Excessive Shyness'. Once the dog has overcome the problem causing their shyness, they will be allowed to take the test again.

- Modifications to this test can be made at the judge's discretion for breed-specific concerns (such as Greyhounds not being required to sit).

- Food may be used as a reward during the test, but not as a lure (Handlers are allowed to lure their dogs into positions without food). Food is allowed between exercises. An exercise is considered complete when the team has performed all the principal features of the exercise. Food may not be given once the team has begun the next exercise.

- Touch rewards and verbal encouragement are highly recommended and are acceptable at any time during the test.

- Harsh verbal or physical corrections are not allowed during the test and will result in the handler being excused. A harsh verbal or physical correction shall be defined as one that offends the sensibilities of the judge or that causes an obvious adverse reaction in the dog.

- Handler teams are allowed three attempts at each exercise. A fail at the first and second attempt will not be noted. A failure on the third attempt will be 'failure to complete exercise'.

- Handlers are allowed to issue a command to their dog three times per exercise attempt. A verbal command combined with or followed by a hand signal is considered to be one command. After the third command, it is considered another attempt.

- There is no maximum running time for the test.

- A flat buckle collar is recommended for the test. Also allowed are martingales, harnesses, chest harnesses, or any other type of humane handling collar. The judge will make the final decision regarding the acceptance of a collar.

Collars not allowed are:

- Halters (unfortunately these cannot be used in therapy work due to their appearance as 'muzzles', which can cause people to make negative assumptions about the dog)

- Choke chains of any kind

- Prong collars

- Any kind of collar that may cause pain to the dog (accidental or intentional)

Dog Obedience Testing Score Sheet

Handler name:

Animal Name:

Exercise	Pass	Pass 2nd Attempt	Pass 3rd Attempt	Relationship Bonus	Failure to complete	Failure – Overly Shy	Failure – Aggression	Failure – Harsh correction
Accept approach: friendly stranger								
Accept petting								
Accept exam.								
Sit								
Down								
Sit Stay								
Down Stay								
Come								
Heel								
Settle								
Total								

Result (circle 1)   Pass with flying colors   Pass   Try again   Failure

Comments and signature:

Small Animal Evaluation Exercises

Accept the approach of a friendly stranger – Allow an unknown person to approach it and speak to the handler in a natural, everyday situation.

Accept petting – Accept an unthreatening stranger touching it. The evaluator will approach the team, request permission to pet the animal, and proceed to touch the animal on the head and body. Following this, the evaluator will inspect the ears, teeth, and eyes, and gently pick up each front foot. The animal may change positions but may not show shyness or aggression.

Be carried by handler while the handler walks – The handler will walk around the test area while carrying the companion animal in both no traffic and light pedestrian activity situations.

Demonstrate calm reactions to distractions – The animal remains calm when faced with everyday distractions. The team will be exposed to two distractions – one visual and one sound.

To evaluate the animal's relationship with the handler:

Awareness of one another and interaction are important elements of a desirable bond between handler and animal. Demonstration of such interaction provides the evaluator with the information necessary to rate the team. Evaluators will be watching for positive interaction between the handler and animal. Handlers are encouraged to interact with their animal and offer encouragement at any time it is deemed appropriate or necessary. Praise and talking to the animal while the team is working is desirable. An animal should be aware of its handler and be responsive to the handler's spoken word and touch. An animal that ignores the handler demonstrates a weak bond. Likewise, a handler who is unaware of the animal's reaction to surroundings demonstrates the lack of a bond with the animal.

Small Animal Obedience Testing Score Sheet

Handler name: _____   Animal Name: _____

Exercise	Pass	Pass 2nd Attempt	Pass 3rd Attempt	Relationship Bonus	Failure to complete	Failure – Overly Shy	Failure – Aggression	Failure – Harsh correction
Accept approach								
Accept petting								
Accept examination								
Heel pattern held by								
Calm reaction to distraction								

Result (circle 1):   Pass with flying colors   Pass   Try again   Failure

Comments and signature:

Canine Good Neighbor Test

The 12 exercises are:
1. Accepting a friendly stranger - I will walk up and introduce myself and shake handler's hand
2. Politely accepts petting - I ask if I may pet your dog and then do so on the head
3. Appearance and grooming - I check the dog for cleanliness and grooming. I also lift the dog's feet and brush or comb the dog lightly   (equipment brought by handler).
4. Out for a walk - Short heeling pattern with a turn right and left
5. Walking through a crowd - handler and dog walk past a group of people
6. Sit/Down command and stay in place - dog is on a long line; handler places dog in sit or down, moves up to 20 feet away, then turns and returns to the dog
7. Come when called - handler again leaves dog and turns and calls dog.
8. Praise and Interaction - handler plays with the dog for short period then settles the dog down on command
9. Reaction to passing dog - handler and dog pass another dog being walked on leash
10. Reaction to distractions - distractions of everyday life are set up, and the dog is walked by them
11. Supervised isolation - handler places dog in a sit or down position and hands leash to someone else. Handler then goes out of sight for 3 minutes. The dog should remain settled for this period - as an evaluator. I do not mind if the dog stands or moves a small amount. I assess not ready when the dog whines, pulls away, or jumps up onto person holding leash
12. Walking through door or gate

HEALTH SCREENING FORM

Handler's name: _____

Companion Animal's Name: _____

Breed _____ Age _____

Intact   Altered

How long have you known the handler? _____

How long have you known this animal?_____

Are you this animal's personal veterinarian?   Yes   No

General Health of Animal:
Excellent = No chronic disease or disorders
Very Good = Minor complaints associated with normal aging
Good = Chronic conditions resulting in occasional flare-ups
Poor = Chronic illness requiring ongoing treatment

How frequently do you see this animal?
Once a year
Regular wellness program
Only when ill/injured
Every _____ months
Other _____

Temp._____   Pulse_____   Resp. _____   Weight_____

Please list any medication(s) currently prescribed: _____
_____

Physical Examination
Check N for Normal findings, A for Abnormal findings. Circle
observations about the dog's general health, paying particular
attention to areas which might affect the dog's ability to visit
safely. Note any physical problems which may put the dog at
risk (e.g. arthritis, painful ear infection, etc.).

SYSTEM	N	A	EXAM FINDINGS	COMMENTS
General Appearance			alert // interested // weak // depressed // overweight // dirty	
Skin/ Coat			shiny coat // healthy skin // hair loss // fleas // itchy // redness // scaly // sores	
Musculo-Skeletal			appears sound // pain // lameness // joint problems	
Heart/ Lungs			strong beat // murmur // fast // slow // clear // breathing problems // cough // rapid respirations // congestion	
Digestive System			normal bowel sounds // pain // enlarged organ // gas // full or painful anal sacs	
Urogenital			normal appearance // abnormal discharge // pain // enlarged prostate	
Eyes/Ears			clear // alert // adequate tearing // discharge // inflamed // cataracts // infection // lid deformities // clean // extra hair	
Nervous System			alert // happy // depressed // abnormal nerve tests	
Lymph Nodes			normal size // swollen	
Mucous Membranes			normal appearance // jaundiced // pale // inflamed	
Teeth/ Mouth			clean // no abnormal odour // tarter // gingivitis // odour // plaque	

Parasite Program: Please list any preventative programs or testing and treatments for controlling parasites (type of parasite, method of control/preventative, frequency):

External (fleas, ticks, etc.) _____

Internal (ascarids, heartworm, etc.) _____

Fecal Exam: (NOTE: A fecal exam is mandatory)

Result: ___ positive ___ negative Date _____

Immunization (or Titer test)

Immunization	Date	Signature of Licensed Veterinarian
Rabies		
Other (at discretion of veteriarian)		

NOTE: If inoculations are not administered, please explain:

_____

Please provide any comments you feel pertains to this animal's participation in a pet therapy program.

VETERINARIAN'S CERTIFICATION
I hereby certify that I have examined the above dog and to the best of my knowledge find the animal physically and mentally healthy and free of contagious diseases.

_____   _____
(signature)   (date)

Name: _____

Clinic: _____

Address: _____

_____

Telephone: _____

Temperament Test
For Animals In Mental Health Settings

Handler's name: _____

Companion Animal's Name: _____

Breed _____ Age _____

                  Intact   Altered

Date of Test: _____

Evaluator/s: _____

Important Notes

> All tests are performed on leash or off-leash at the discretion of the evaluator with the owner/handler in the testing area.
>
> Dogs are evaluated on the basis of acceptable and unacceptable responses to each of the tests. A dog whose response is acceptable but exhibits stress or discomfort will be considered 'borderline.' Should a dog exhibit borderline responses in more than three (3) tests, the dog will be considered unsuitable for animal-assisted therapy in a mental health setting.
>
> Any dog that growls, barks, snaps, bites, or lunges at a person will be considered unsuitable for animal-assisted therapy in a mental health setting.
>
> Any dog that touches anyone with his teeth or feet will be considered unsuitable for animal-assisted therapy in a mental health setting.
>
> Any dog that eliminates during the testing will be considered unsuitable for animal-assisted therapy in a mental health setting.

Description	Accept-able	Unaccept-able	Border-line	Comments
Test #1. Handled by Stranger Evaluator: look in ears, hold tail, put fingers in mouth, handle feet				
Test #2. Exuberant/Clumsy Petting Evaluator: repeat petting/manipulation using stronger, more aggressive pressure. Exuberantly speak in high-pitched voice; squeal; jiggle the animal; handle feet. Pet using an inanimate object.				
Test #3. Hand-Shy Evaluator: unexpectedly move hand directly at the animal's head in a quick motion.				
Test #4. Restraining Hug Evaluator: unexpectedly, give the animal a full body hug that restricts its movement.				
Test #5. Pain Response Evaluator: pet the animal, then, unexpectedly, pinch the it between the toes or on the flank.				
Test #6. Direct Stare Evaluator: stare directly at the animal until the animal breaks the stare and averts its eyes.				
Test #7. Bumped From Behind While the animal is distracted, evaluator: bump into the animal's body from behind. If very small, a hard stomp or loud slap made behind the animal.				
Test #8. Loud, Angry Vocalization (indirect) Evaluator: shout and wave arms approx. 2 m. from animal without making eye contact.				

Description	Accept-able	Unaccept-able	Border-line	Comments
Test #9. Loud, Angry Vocalization (direct) Repeat #8, making direct eye contact with animal.				
Test #10. Sitting with Stranger (touching) Evaluator: sit in chair, while handler asks the animal to 'go see;' the evaluator will pet and talk to the animal (for 3 min.)				
Test #11. Sitting with Stranger (not touching) Repeat #10, without petting or talking to animal.				
Test #12. Reaction to Movement Evaluator: sit in a chair and swing an extremity in the proximity of the animal.				
Test #13. Taking a Treat Evaluator: offer a treat by finger pinch and by open hand.				
Cautionary				
Test #14. Blow In Face Evaluator: unexpectedly, blow into animal's face.				
Test #15. Feet Stomping Evaluator and at least 1 other person: walk around animal in a wide circle (at least 2 m. away) stomping feet loudly.				
Test #16. Reaction to Running/Being Chased Evaluator: run past the animal; if it begins to run, the evaluator will chase the animal.				
Test #17. Play/Settle Evaluator: excite the dog with enthusiastic play for up to 1 min., then terminate the interaction.				

Description	Accept-able	Unaccept-able	Border-line	Comments
Test #18. Crowded Petting Evaluator and 2 other persons: gather closely around the animal and touch it. All talk at once, trying to gain the animal's attention.				
Test #19. Come When Called (other than handler) Evaluator and 2 other persons: stand at least 3 m. from the animal and call it to come, one at a time.				
Summary: